MORE ORIGAMI
WITH EXPLANATIONS

Fun with Folding and Math

MORE ORIGAMI WITH EXPLANATIONS

Fun with Folding and Math

Jeanine Meyer

SUNY Purchase, USA

Takashi Mukoda

 **World Scientific**

NEW JERSEY · LONDON · SINGAPORE · BEIJING · SHANGHAI · HONG KONG · TAIPEI · CHENNAI · TOKYO

Published by

World Scientific Publishing Co. Pte. Ltd.

5 Toh Tuck Link, Singapore 596224

USA office: 27 Warren Street, Suite 401-402, Hackensack, NJ 07601

UK office: 57 Shelton Street, Covent Garden, London WC2H 9HE

Library of Congress Cataloging-in-Publication Data
Names: Meyer, Jeanine, author. | Mukoda, Takashi, author.
Title: More origami with explanations : fun with folding and math / Jeanine Meyer,
    SUNY Purchase, USA, Takashi Mukoda.
Description: New Jersey : World Scientific, [2021] | Includes index.
Identifiers: LCCN 2020042634 | ISBN 9789811220081 (hardcover) | ISBN 9789811219467 (paperback) |
    ISBN 9789811219474 (ebook for institutions) | ISBN 9789811219481 (ebook for individuals)
Subjects: LCSH: Origami. | Origami--Mathematics. | Origami in education. | Mathematics--Study and teaching.
Classification: LCC QA491 .M483 2021 | DDC 736/.982--dc23
LC record available at https://lccn.loc.gov/2020042634

British Library Cataloguing-in-Publication Data
A catalogue record for this book is available from the British Library.

Cover design by Takashi Mukoda

For any available supplementary material, please visit
https://www.worldscientific.com/worldscibooks/10.1142/11803#t=suppl

Desk Editors: Tan Rok Ting/Ramya Gangadharan

Typeset by Stallion Press
Email: enquiries@stallionpress.com

Dedication to the teachers

*Lillian Oppenheimer, Michael Shall,
Laura Kruskal, Mark Kennedy*

Preface

Origami, paper folding, originated hundreds of years ago in China and Japan, with independent discoveries across the world. Today people engage in origami, create new models, share their work, and discover mathematical principles in the process. This book continues the approach of *Origami with Explanations*; but is independent, with basic instructions repeated. The models in this book include action models, money folds, beautiful and useful containers, and modular origami.

Each chapter starts with the *Background* section and includes photos of the final models. When the model is not considered traditional and the designer/inventor are known, they are credited. The authors have striven to be accurate with attributions and would appreciate any corrections and amendments.

The Instruction section has text, photos, marked up photos, and diagrams (after description of standard origami diagramming). Unlike most origami books, we do not strive for brevity, but use techniques such as providing photos with the positions of hands and fingers, and may include diagrams and photos for the same steps.

The *Explanations* section follows, in which origami and mathematics reinforce each other to provide understanding of the folding procedures. Note that we take a broad view of mathematics. The experiences in spatial relations provided by doing origami are reinforced by attention to symmetries and the transitions from 2D to 3D. Other mathematics topics include improving estimates, tessellations, and mathematical induction. Peeks (teasers) are given into the origami mathematical topics of flat-foldability and fold-and-cut.

The *Enhancements and Next Steps* section provides suggestions for adding to the beauty and use of the models. It also has a preview of the next section. The *Exercises and Explorations* section offers activities for experiences building on the material in the chapter. Throughout the text, there are *Tips* for readers, parents and teachers, including suggestions on supplies. There is also an *Index*.

The text is suitable for individual reading as well as use in classes, home-schooling, and special programs. It will serve people with no background in origami and those who want to broaden and deepen their understanding and skill. We report that many of our students tell us that the material made them appreciate, even enjoy, math topics they had avoided in the past. They also report enjoying time away from screens.

About the Authors

 **Jeanine Meyer** is Professor Emerita at Purchase College/ State University of New York, USA. Before moving to academia, Jeanine worked at IBM Research and other companies. She earned her PhD in Computer Science at New York University; an MA in Mathematics at Columbia University, and graduated Magna Cum Laude from the University of Chicago, majoring in Mathematics. Jeanine has authored or co-authored 8 books in computing and mathematics, plus two updates.

 **Takashi Mukoda** is a graduate of Purchase College/State University of New York, majoring both in Mathematics/ Computer Science and in New Media. He won the State University of New York Chancellor's Award and other honors. He now works as a Frontend engineer in Tokyo, Japan.

 The collaboration between the two authors started with Takashi working as technical reviewer for three of Jeanine's books on programming. Takashi contributed to the design of the Purchase College general education course on origami and mathematics before the start of the course and was one of the class teaching assistants for the first class in Spring 2019. Jeanine recruited him to be co-author after his return to Japan.

Acknowledgments

We acknowledge the work of Lillian Oppenheimer, Sam Ciulla, Laura Kruskal, Peter Engel, Junior Fritz Jacquet, Tomoko Fuse, Gay Merrill Gross, Robert Neale, Martin Kruskal, Phillip Shen, Paul Jackson, David Mitchell, and Jo Nakashima. We thank them along with family members Kish Shen and Karen Kruskal and Clyde Kruskal for granting us permission to feature their work in our books.

We also want to acknowledge and thank readers and people who gave us advice and encouragement: Gay Merrill Gross, Robert Lang, Jeremy Shafer, David Brill, David Mitchell, Rona Gurkewitz, Julianna Biro, Jan Polish (of OrigamiUSA), Gilad Aharoni (Gilad's List), Dr. Florence Mann, Alexander Kellerman, Joey Kellerman, Nico Kellerman and others. They are not responsible for any mistakes.

We want to thank Purchase College/SUNY colleagues Knarik Tunyan and Irina Shablinsky, for suggesting doing the origami mathematics general education class and their considerable help to us both over the years.

Contents

Chapter 1

Kissy Fish

Background

The model for this chapter is the Kissy Fish (sometimes called the Talking Fish) designed by Junior Fritz Jacquet from the Piranha by Jun Maekawa. See Figure 1.1. It is an action model and fun. The model provides an opportunity to explain different ways of dividing an edge into thirds. It also requires a sink fold, which is a technique to master for more complex models.

Figure 1.1.   Kissy Fish.

1

SUPPLIES

Kissy Fish

Square paper, such as origami kami paper, would be fine. White lips and inside of mouth look okay. DUO paper—two non-white colors—would be okay for this model. We suggest starting with 10-inch. This is a model that people like to make of different sizes.

Instructions

Start with the white side up, oriented as a diamond, and make a diagonal fold. Figure 1.2 is a typical origami diagram. The arrow shows the direction of folding and also that the top point is to be placed on top of the bottom point. The dashed lines indicate a valley fold. If we looked at the folding in process, we would see a valley. If we turned the paper over, we would see a mountain and call it a mountain fold.

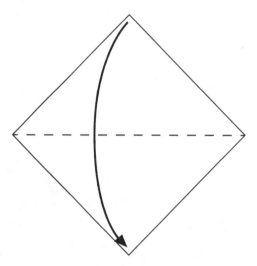

Figure 1.2. Making the first diagonal fold.

See Figure 1.3. Here, we introduce some symbols generally used in origami diagrams. For those who have already read our first book, **Origami With Explanations**, now is a good time to recall how we used the following symbols in the diagrams for other models.

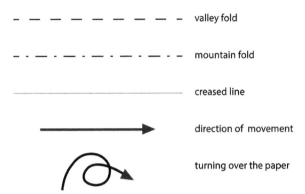

— — — — — — — — — valley fold

— · — · — · — · — · — mountain fold

_____ creased line

——————————➤ direction of movement

⟲ turning over the paper

Figure 1.3. Symbols used in origami diagrams.

Focus on the horizontal, folded edge at the top. We need to divide the edge into thirds. How can this be done? Of course, it is possible to measure that length of the edge, but it turns out that there are other ways there are effective, and, once you master them, quicker. We will describe one way here and include the explanation for why it works along with two other methods in the Explanations section.

Make an estimate, a guess, at what you think is one-third of the length of the whole edge, starting from the left. Make a pinch mark A at that point. (a pinch is a small crease—not from edge to edge. It will be used as a landmark for a subsequent fold.) Figure 1.4 shows a photo. Note: the pinch is a valley fold.

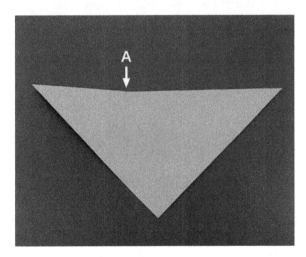

Figure 1.4. Mark A at the estimate of one-third from the left.

Now, bring the right corner over to the pinch mark A and make a pinch mark there (Figure 1.5). See Figure 1.6 where this second pinch mark is labeled B.

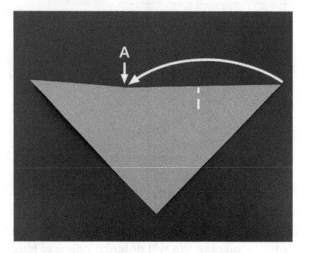

Figure 1.5.   Arrow indicating to bring the right corner to A.

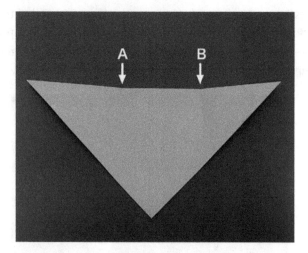

Figure 1.6.   Mark B after bringing the right point over to the pinch mark A.

Bring the left side over to B. Make a new pinch mark. Call this one C. What is going on, to be explained in detail later, is that this procedure improves the estimate. Now bring the right side over to point C and make a pinch at the half way point. This will make a mark near point B. Call this mark D. Now bring the left side over to D and make a pinch at the half way point. Keep going from side to side.

Each iteration improves the estimate. You stop when there is no change. You have pinch marks at one-third of the distance from each end of the edge. See Figures 1.7 and 1.8.

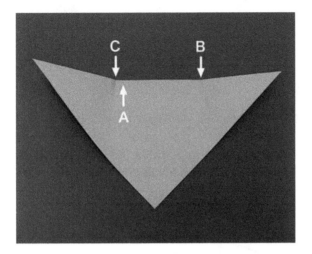

Figure 1.7. Mark C that is more improved estimation than A.

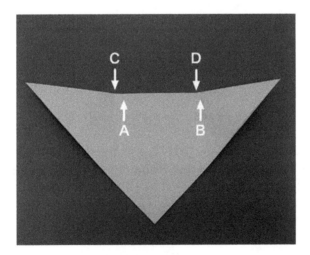

Figure 1.8. Mark D that is more improved estimation than B.

Figure 1.9 shows the directions to make valley folds at the point one-third of the way from the left side and two-thirds of the way from the left side, which also is one-third of the way from the right side. Make one complete valley fold; unfold; make the other complete valley fold; and unfold.

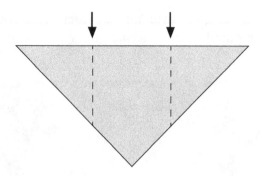

Figure 1.9.   Valley folds at one-third from the left and one-third from the right.

Figure 1.10 shows the next step: divide the model in half by folding the right corner over to the left. The diagram follows the standard origami diagramming by showing the previous folds as thin, solid lines. The next fold is indicated by the arrow and the dashed lines, representing a valley fold.

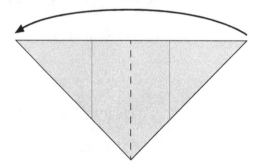

Figure 1.10.   Dividing the model in half.

The result is shown in Figure 1.11. The instruction in this diagram is to fold a corner over to line up with the line made by the thirds operation. Figure 1.12 shows the result.

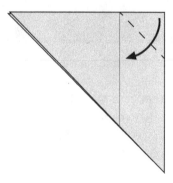

Figure 1.11.   Folding a corner over to the crease line.

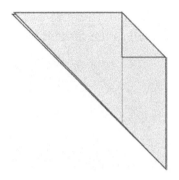

Figure 1.12. Result of the previous fold.

Now unfold everything. Figure 1.13 shows the results, with the sense (mountain vs valley) of each fold. Mountain folds are dashes and dots. Note: often in origami diagrams, the crease lines of previous folds are shown as thin lines. However here, we want to make you aware of the different sense of the creases.

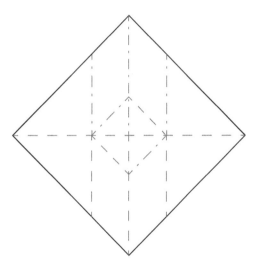

Figure 1.13. Sense of all the previous folds.

Notice that the vertical lines are part mountain and part valley and the middle diamond has both mountain fold and valley fold creases. This is because the folds were made to a folded triangle. The next step is to do what is called a sink fold on the square diamond in the middle. The sink fold is what the name indicates: part of the paper is sunk into the model. In preparation for doing the sink, we need to change some of the folds (the creases to be changed are indicated as bold lines in the diagram below) so the sense is as indicated in Figure 1.14.

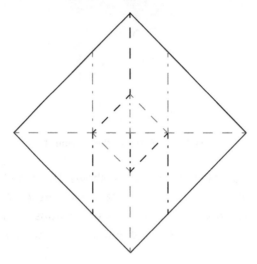

Figure 1.14.   Change some senses of the previous folds as indicated (one side).

The square diamond in the middle diamond should be all valley folds. Some of the other folds are to be changed as well. Turn the model over (Figure 1.15).

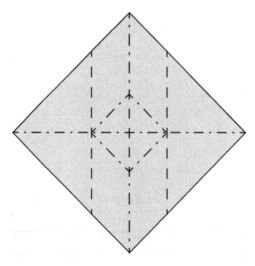

Figure 1.15.   Change sense of some of the previous folds as indicated (the other side).

As you would expect, turning the model over changes the sense of each fold. For example, on the color side, the edges of the middle square diamond are all mountain folds. Figure 1.16 shows Takashi changing the sense of one of the creases.

Figure 1.16. Making all the edges of the middle square diamond into mountain folds.

The objective now is to make the center point of the square diamond sink into the inside of the model. See Figures 1.17–1.19.

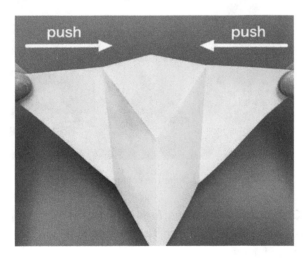

Figure 1.17. Pushing the model from the both sides to sink the square diamond.

Figure 1.18. Pushing in process.

Figure 1.19. Done the collapsing procedure.

Figure 1.20 shows the collapsed model, with the next step indicated. This step is to make a MOUNTAIN fold bisecting the angle (Figure 1.21). We are wrapping the flap around itself.

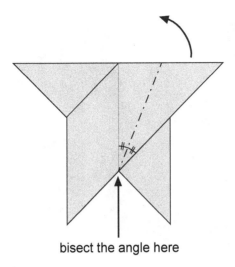

bisect the angle here

Figure 1.20.   Mountain fold bisecting the indicated angle.

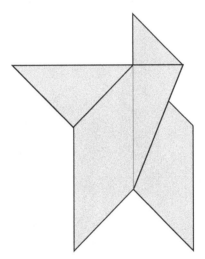

Figure 1.21.   Result of the previous fold.

Turn the model over and do the same thing by bisecting the angle with a mountain fold. As you look down the model from the top, you can see radial symmetry. See Figure 1.22.

Figure 1.22.   Model seen from the top showing radial symmetry.

Figure 1.23 shows the results of the two mountain fold steps.

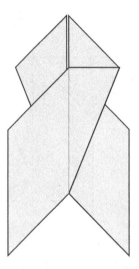

Figure 1.23.   Results of the two mountain fold steps.

The next step is to twist the upper parts to form the fins. Make a mountain fold on an indicated line in Figure 1.24.

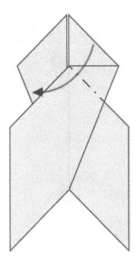

Figure 1.24. Mountain fold to make a fin.

Then, open up the upper parts and wrap into what we have just made as shown in Figures 1.25 and 1.26.

Figure 1.25. Seen from the top.

Figure 1.26.   One of the fins is completed.

Turn the model over. Then repeat the previous step to make another fin as indicated in Figures 1.27–1.29.

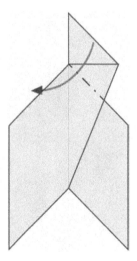

Figure 1.27.   Mountain fold to make another fin.

Figure 1.28.   Making another fin in process.

Figure 1.29.   Seen from the top.

The result of the last two steps is shown in Figure 1.30.

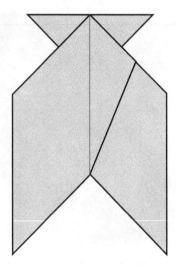

Figure 1.30.   Fins are completed.

The model definitely is fish-like now. Figure 1.31 (will refer to this point in the Exercises) indicates the forming of the lips. Doing this requires preparation folds as indicated: valley fold on each side of the mouth. The valley folds are made on two layers.

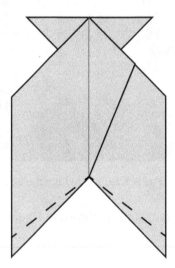

Figure 1.31.   Valley fold lines for preparation folds.

Now, using the same crease lines, turn the lips inside-out. This is called an outside reverse fold. The paper is made to go outside of the rest of the model. See Figures 1.32 and 1.33.

Figure 1.32. Turning a lip inside-out in process.

Figure 1.33. Done one of the lips.

Now form the cleft in the lips by folding down the corners as shown in Figures 1.34–1.36.

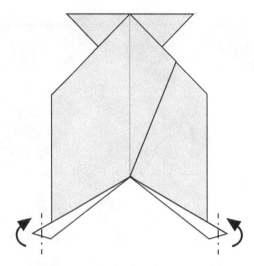

Figure 1.34.   Forming the cleft in the lips.

Figure 1.35.   Forming the cleft in process.

Figure 1.36. The cleft is completed.

Figure 1.37 shows the results.

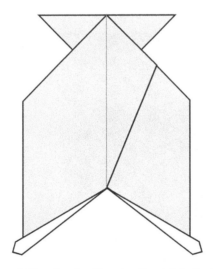

Figure 1.37. Result of forming the cleft in the lips.

We call the next step: throat surgery. Pick up the model and look down the throat as shown in Figure 1.38.

Figure 1.38.   The throat of the fish model.

Move the fold sticking up in the throat to one side. See Figure 1.39. The desired result is shown in Figure 1.40.

Figure 1.39.   Insert finger in the throat.

Figure 1.40. Result of the throat surgery.

Your Fish is done. You operate it as shown in Figure 1.41.

Figure 1.41. Final model of the Kissy Fish.

Explanations

Three methods of dividing an edge into thirds

#1 Iterative method

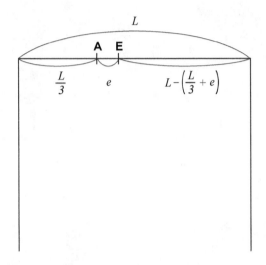

Figure 1.42. Diagram with labels and indicating the necessary distances.

Figure 1.42 shows a line segment, measuring *L* units in some system. (For this explanation, any system of measurement will do.) The point with the label A indicates the actual location of one-third the distance. We mark here a point E which represents our estimate. In this explanation, our estimate is further than A from the end. A similar argument can be made for an estimate that is less than one-third. The distance from the left end to A is *L*/3. The distance to E is represented by the expression: *L*/3 + *e*. The *e* is the error term, how much the estimate is wrong, so *e* is a good choice of symbol, but it and all the other symbols could be anything.

The next step of the process is to fold the other end of the paper to E. This divides the length of paper from the other end to E in half. We now calculate (symbolically) the length from the other end to E. It is *L* − (*L*/3 + *e*).

$$L - \left(\frac{L}{3} + e \right) = L - \frac{L}{3} - e = \frac{2}{3}L - e$$

The next step is to divide each side of the equation by 2:

$$\left(\frac{2}{3}L-e\right)\times\frac{1}{2}=\frac{L}{3}-\frac{e}{2}$$

This result is indicating that the step of folding to the estimate produces a point B that is $e/2$ from the actual value. This is a situation in which if you don't give a little jump, you probably did not understand it. The mark B made by this step of the folding produces a BETTER estimate. The error term has been halved. Continuing this process halves the error term each time. What this means in terms of actual folding is that at some point, the new mark is the same as the prior mark. We/you have divided the edge into thirds! A negative feature of this approach is the multiple pinches. See Figure 1.43.

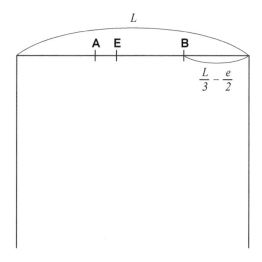

Figure 1.43.   Diagram indicating the distance between B and the right corner.

Iterative procedures such as this are used in engineering all the time!

#2 The S method of thirds

Another method of determining thirds is called the S method, though Z is more descriptive. You work to line up the edge to resemble an S or Z and then flatten it. Figures 1.44 and 1.45 show a sequence. It is an iterative method in that you gradually work the edge into position.

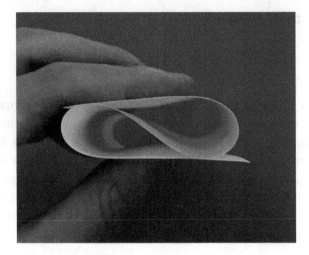

Figure 1.44.   S (Z) method in process.

Figure 1.45.   S (Z) method is completed.

Note that the folds at one-third and two-thirds are different: one valley and one mountain. So you need to change that if it is not what you want (Figure 1.46).

Figure 1.46. Unfold the folds created by S (Z) method: one is valley and the other is mountain.

#3 Geometric method of thirds

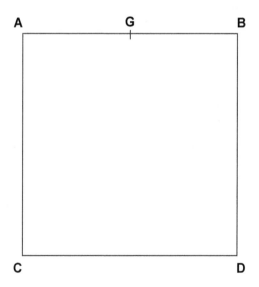

Figure 1.47. Square with labels.

The geometric method requires dividing a square in half with a book fold and making a diagonal fold. Figure 1.47 shows a square ABDC. The point G is halfway between A and B. We use a different technique here from the branch of mathematics called analytical geometry. This is a reminder, if you have seen this already, or an introduction. Think of it as a teaser to what is possible with analytical geometry techniques. The square is not a shape floating in space but on a plane with a coordinate system. In Figure 1.48, there is a horizontal axis, labeled the *x*-axis, and a vertical axis, labeled the *y*-axis. The points can be represented by two numbers: the *x* position and the *y* position. In our example, C is at the origin. Its coordinates—you can think of this as an address—are (0, 0). The point A is at the same *x* position but away (above) it vertically. Its coordinates are (0, 1). The point B is at (1, 1) and the point D is at (1, 0). See Figure 1.48 and look these over one at a time to see if it makes sense to you. Note: our choice of coordinates for A, B, and D, given that we put point C at (0, 0) was up to us. We could have used, (0, 100), (100, 100), and (100, 0).

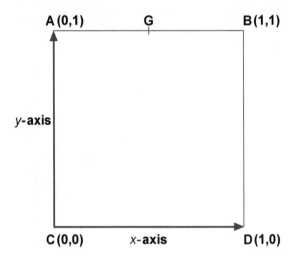

Figure 1.48.   Indicating coordinates at each corner.

We can now write equations for the line going from A to D and the line going from C to G. We will then determine their intersection. This will show that the intersection is at the 1/3 point.

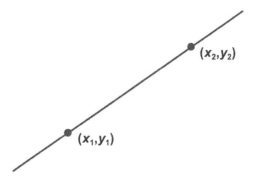

Figure 1.49. Coordinates used to describe how to calculate the distance between two points.

First of all, we need to know how to get an equation of a line going through two points. The two points are represented by (x_1, y_1) and (x_2, y_2) as indicated in the Figure 1.49. The standard format is

$$y - y_1 = \frac{y_2 - y_1}{x_2 - x_1}(x - x_1)$$

You may recall if you have seen anything like this before, that $(y_2 - y_1)/(x_2 - x_1)$ is the slope of the line.

The point C is at (0, 0) and the point G is at (1/2, 1). Using the standard, the equation for the line CG is

$$y - 0 = \frac{1 - 0}{1/2 - 0}(x - 0)$$

$$y = \frac{1}{1/2}x$$

$$y = 2x$$

This passes our test for being reasonable: the y values are proportional to the x values, but y is increases twice as fast as x.

The coordinates of the points A and D are (0, 1) and (1, 0), so the equation for the line AD is

$$y - 1 = \frac{0 - 1}{1 - 0}(x - 0)$$

$$y - 1 = -x$$

$$y = -x + 1$$

This also passes a reasonableness test: the slope is negative: the line is going down. Larger values of x are paired with smaller value of y. We also can check if the equation works at A and at D and it does. When x is 0, y is 1. When x is 1, y is 0.

So now we have two equations. The intersection must satisfy both equations. To determine what x value satisfies both equations, we set

$$2x = -x + 1$$

This is "saying," suppose the y's are the same, then what is the value of x? Solving the equation, we first add x to both sides to get

$$2x + x = (-x + 1) + x$$

$$3x = 1$$

Solving this be dividing by 3

$$3x / 3 = 1/3$$

$$x = 1/3$$

Now, we are not saying this is a good approach for the Kissy Fish, but it could be good if the folding procedure involves the whole square paper and the diagonal and the book fold have been done. One could start to fold the line from C to G and make a pinch at the intersection with the diagonal (Figure 1.50).

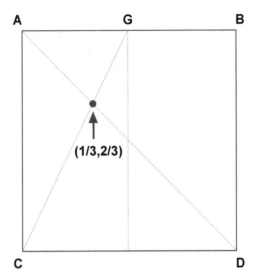

Figure 1.50. Coordinate at the intersection of line AD and line CG.

Sinks and Outside Reverse Folds

Sinks and outside reverse folds have something in common with each other and also other basic folds: each involve making preparation folds and then using those folds to re-position a portion of the model. The re-positioning involves folding on existing crease lines but changing the sense (mountain or valley) of some of the folds. In our first book, **Origami with Explanations**, we show examples of reverse folds, (also called inside reverse fold) and petal folds and they share these characteristics. The benefits from learning the terms is that you can remember each of them as one thing instead of two or more operations.

Enhancements and Next Steps

The Kissy Fish is an appropriate model for decorating. It also is a frequent choice to make different sizes and to display a bigger fish eating a smaller fish. Note also that there are other fish in the origami sea.

In a later chapter, you will learn a similar iterative procedure for dividing the edge of a dollar bill into elevenths!

The next chapter features models of tetrahedrons, four-sided polyhedron objects. The Tetrahedron model (by Jo Nakashima) is made by folding a strip of paper. A second model is called *Rotating Tetrahedrons*, by Tomoko Fuse, and features 3 double tetrahedrons, joined together, that can rotate.

Exercises and Explorations

1. Look up inside reverse (also called simply reverse), outside reverse, squash, petal, and sink folds in our book or others, and practice making them. Teach the Kissy Fish and other models having these folds to someone else and report on what teaching strategies worked well and what did not.
2. Find and learn the Piranha model by Jun Maekawa. How is it different from the Kissy Fish?
3. Why did we need to perform the throat surgery?
4. Unfold the model, being careful around the lips, or make the model only to Figure 1.30 and unfold. Try to calculate the final dimensions.

Chapter 2

Tetrahedrons

Background

The models for this chapter involve *tetrahedrons*. A tetrahedron is a type of *polyhedron*. A polyhedron is a solid shape made up of vertices, edges and faces, with each face a polygon. A polygon is a two dimensional shape, that is, it lies in a plane. Rectangles and triangles are polygons. The edges are straight lines. Polyhedrons are the three dimensional versions of polygons. Polyhedrons consist of vertices, edges and faces and the faces are polygons. A cube is a polyhedron. A sphere is not, just like a circle is not a polygon.

A tetrahedron is a polyhedron with four faces (*tetra* is Greek for four), each face a triangle. A *regular tetrahedron* is one in which all four of its faces are regular triangles, meaning the sides of each triangle, which correspond to edges of the solid, are all the same length. In fact, all the edges of the solid are the same length. Note that there is another term for regular triangles, namely *equilateral triangles*. This means that the angles are all the same, which, in turn, means that each angle is 60 degrees as shown in Figure 2.1 because the sum of the angles is 180 degrees. A tetrahedron is an example of a *Platonic Solid* and this is discussed in the Explanations section.

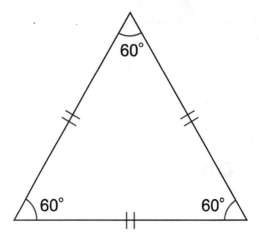

Figure 2.1.   Right triangle (equilateral triangle).

The first model in this chapter is a tetrahedron constructed by folding up a strip of paper. The designer is Jo Nakashima. See Figure 2.2.

Figure 2.2.   Tetrahedrons constructed from strips of paper.

The other model is made from three sheets of paper and is called *Rotating Tetrahedrons* designed by Tomoko Fuse. See Figure 2.3.

Figure 2.3. Rotating tetrahedron.

The model consists of six tetrahedrons made out of three sheets of paper.

SUPPLIES

Single Tetrahedron
A long strip of paper. We found that dividing 8.5 × 14, also called Legal size in the USA, into fifths and cutting the paper to make strips works.

Rotating Tetrahedron
Three pieces of kami, five or six inches, three different colors work well. Foil also works.

Instructions

Tetrahedron

Orient the strip so the long sides are at the top and bottom.

The first step of making a tetrahedron out of a strip is folding the strip long side to long side but just making a pinch to mark the halfway mark close to the left end, say about 1/2 the height of the strip to 1.5 times the height of the strip as shown in Figure 2.4. You do not need to measure the pinch.

Figure 2.4. Pinch mark.

The next step is to fold the bottom left corner to the pinch. See Figure 2.5. We are going to make a valley fold AD by bringing the point C to E. The result is shown in Figure 2.6.

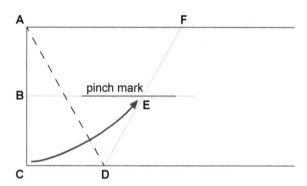

Figure 2.5. Fold the bottom left corner to the pinch in order to making a triangle ADE.

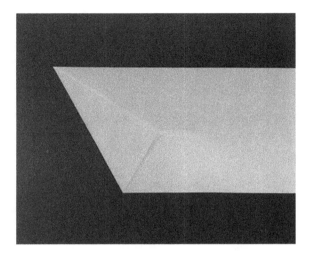

Figure 2.6.   Result of the previous fold.

Look at your model to see a triangle corresponding to the ADF triangle in Figure 2.7. A valley fold is indicated by a line from D to F. Make this fold. You are folding a triangle to lie flat on the strip. Compare to Figure 2.8.

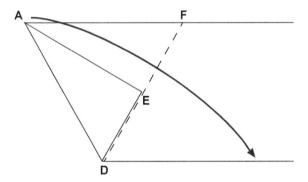

Figure 2.7.   After making a valley fold on a line from D to F.

Figure 2.8.   Result of the previous fold.

The next step is essentially a repeat. See Figure 2.9. We say essentially because the fold line is the side of a triangle, but now slanted upwards. The result of the fold is shown in Figure 2.10.

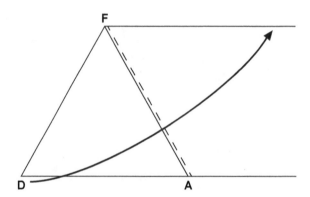

Figure 2.9.   Another valley fold to produce another right triangle.

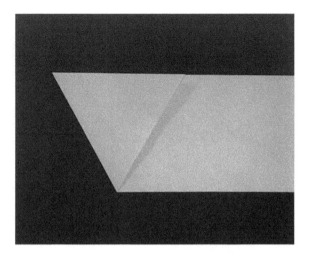

Figure 2.10. Result of the previous fold.

Keep folding the triangles over and over until you get to the end of the strip, that is when there is no more paper to fold. See Figure 2.11 for the next to the last fold of this part of the folding procedure. Crease the folds well. See Figure 2.12 for the last fold.

Figure 2.11. Before the last fold of this repetitive procedure.

Figure 2.12.   Done last fold of this procedure.

Undo all the folds except the very first one. See Figure 2.13.

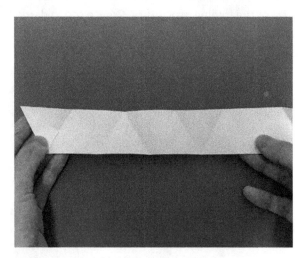

Figure 2.13.   Undo all the folds except for the first one.

The next sequence of folds is along the creases already made but you will be working in 3D, forming the tetrahedron.

Make the first fold, but instead of pressing it flat, keep it vertical. See Figure 2.14.

Figure 2.14. Keep the first fold vertical.

Make the next fold, wrapping the paper around. See Figures 2.15 and 2.16.

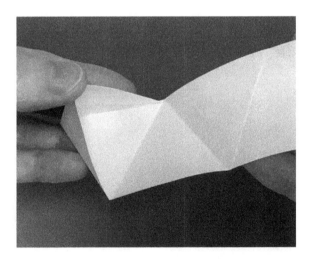

Figure 2.15. Next fold by wrapping the paper around.

Figure 2.16.   Another fold is done. Seen from the top.

Proceed in this manner, but look ahead to stop when there are four triangles remaining on the strip (Figure 2.17).

Figure 2.17.   Four triangles left.

Now, reverse direction, making the next fold wrapping the model in the opposite direction. In other words, we are changing the sense of folds from valley to mountain (Figure 2.18).

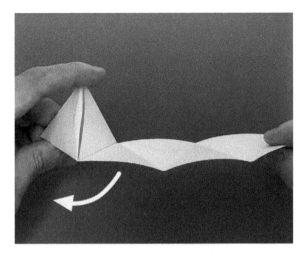

Figure 2.18. Change the sense of folds to mountain.

Continue see Figures 2.19 and 2.20.

Figure 2.19. One mountain fold is done.

Figure 2.20.   Keep wrapping the model.

Continue for the next three triangles, and then push the extra material into the slot. See Figures 2.21 and 2.22.

Figure 2.21.   Extra portion and pocket.

Figure 2.22.   Inserting the extra portion into the pocket.

Here is the final result. It actually is quite robust (Figure 2.23).

Figure 2.23.   Final model of tetrahedron constructed from strips of paper.

Rotating Tetrahedron

The Rotating Tetrahedron model consists of six connected tetrahedron shapes. It is an action model: you can rotate the tetrahedrons! The model requires three sheets of paper. The preparation of each sheet, which we refer to as a unit, is the same.

Take a sheet of paper, white side up, and make one book fold (edge to opposite edge) as indicated in Figure 2.24.

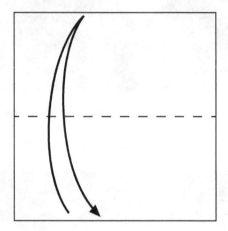

Figure 2.24.   Horizontal book fold.

Unfold. Now make cupboard folds by folding the cut edges to the center crease line as indicated in Figure 2.25. (If you orient the paper so the crease lines are vertical, the cupboard folds resemble a cupboard.)

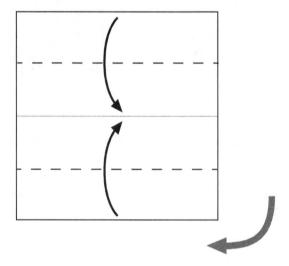

Figure 2.25.   Cupboard folds and arrow indicating to rotate the model by 90 degrees.

Rotate the model by 90 degrees and fold it in half by bringing the bottom edge to the top edge. See Figure 2.26.

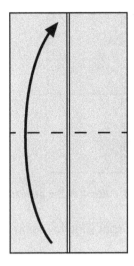

Figure 2.26. Fold the model in half.

Figure 2.27 shows the result and indicates the next fold. Make a valley fold of the top layers.

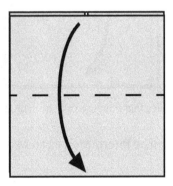

Figure 2.27. Valley fold from top to bottom on the top layers.

Figure 2.28 shows the result, with an arrow to turn the model over.

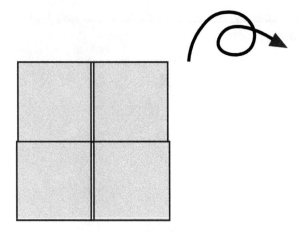

Figure 2.28. Result of the previous valley fold.

Repeat on the other side: that is, follow instructions given in Figure 2.29.

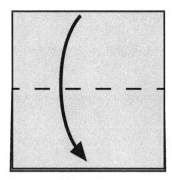

Figure 2.29. Valley fold from top to bottom on the another layers.

You have made what can be interpreted as an M or a W. Figures 2.30 and 2.31 show the result.

Figure 2.30. Unfolded the last two valley folds.

Figure 2.31. M shape seen from the side.

Now unfold the last three folds, returning the paper to just the cupboard folds. Figure 2.32 shows the next set of steps.

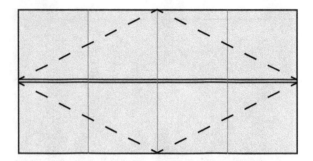

Figure 2.32.   Diagonal folds in small rectangles.

These folds are not that easy to make because they are diagonals but not made by folding a point to an opposite point. They are diagonal folds of the four small rectangles. Figures 2.33–2.35 show the technique of pressing at one corner, than the other corner and then folding in between.

Figure 2.33.   Fix the bottom point.

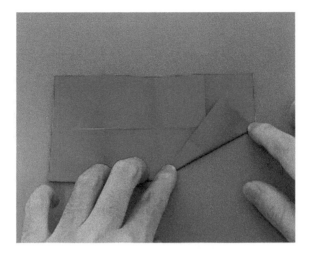

Figure 2.34. Fix the top point.

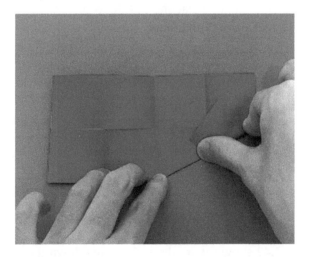

Figure 2.35. Make a crease between the two points.

Unfold the all four diagonal folds. See Figure 2.36.

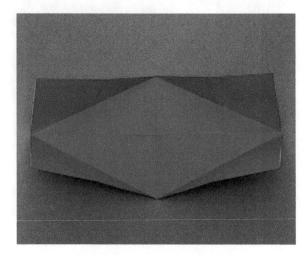

Figure 2.36.   Four diagonals unfolded.

The next step is to fold two diagonals of the whole model. Figure 2.37 shows the valley folds to make and then unfold.

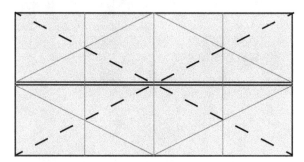

Figure 2.37.   Two diagonal folds in the whole model.

Figures 2.38–2.42 show the method of holding down the center point, then holding one end and then the other end, and then making the fold and, lastly, unfolding.

Figure 2.38. Fix the top point.

Figure 2.39. Fix the bottom point.

Figure 2.40.   Make a crease between the two points.

Figure 2.41.   Turn the model over and repeat the process.

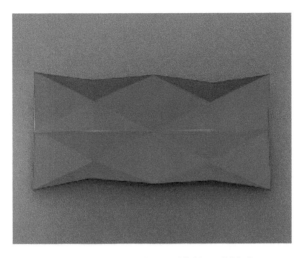

Figure 2.42. Two diagonal folds unfolded.

This is all the folding for one piece of paper, one unit of the model. Repeat for the other two sheets of paper.

The units are put together by weaving them. Open the cupboard folds of one unit and place a second on inside as shown in Figures 2.43 and 2.44.

Figure 2.43. Open the first unit and place the second one onto it.

Figure 2.44.   Close the first unit.

Make sure the second unit is tucked into the midpoint. Close the first unit and now partially open the second to fit in the third unit. See Figures 2.45 and 2.46.

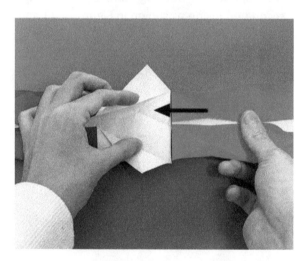

Figure 2.45.   Inserting the third unit into the second one.

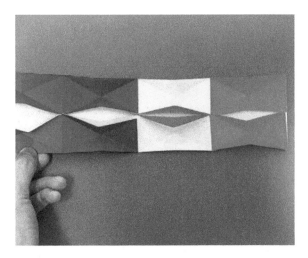

Figure 2.46. All units combined.

Again, make sure the unit is in all the way. Close up the cupboard folds. The next step is to bring the first unit around to tuck into the third unit. Figures 2.47–2.50 show the procedure of inserting the first unit into the third one.

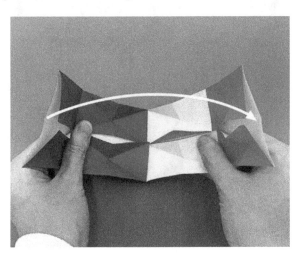

Figure 2.47. Bring the first unit over to the third.

Figure 2.48.   Inserting the first unit into the third.

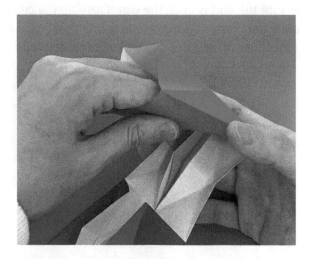

Figure 2.49.   Open the third unit to make a space for the first unit.

Figure 2.50.   Inserting in process.

The challenge here is to get this unit into the midpoint. One technique, suggested by Sara Adams, is to reach inside and put your finger inside of the cupboard fold and then use your other hand to slide the outside up. See Figures 2.51 and 2.52.

Figure 2.51.   Putting a finger inside of the cupboard fold.

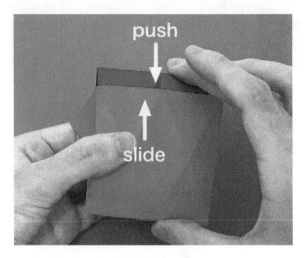

Figure 2.52.   Slide the third unit up and push the first unit down.

The goal is to have the three colors each taking up a whole side. Figure 2.53 shows the results to this point.

Figure 2.53.   Three units are combined. Triangular space seen from the top.

The next series of steps forms the tetrahedrons. You will be reinforcing fold lines on all three units.

On the outside, reinforce a mountain fold as indicated and punch out the marked line so it is NOT a valley fold on each unit. See Figure 2.54. Figure 2.55 shows the line being reinforced.

Figure 2.54. Mountain fold to be reinforced.

Figure 2.55. Reinforce the mountain fold.

Now reinforce the long triangles at the edges of each unit, as indicated in Figure 2.56. See also Figure 2.57.

Figure 2.56.   Mountain fold to be reinforced.

Figure 2.57.   Reinforce the mountain fold.

Push the corners in as shown in Figures 2.58–2.60.

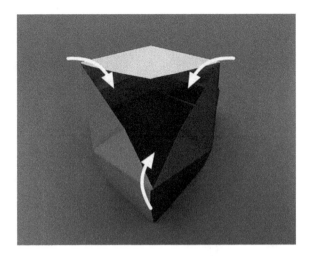

Figure 2.58.   Pushing the sides into.

Figure 2.59.   Pushing in process.

Figure 2.60.   Pushing is done.

Turn the model over and repeat: reinforce the long triangles at the edges of each unit and then push in the corners. See Figures 2.61–2.63.

Figure 2.61.   Pushing the sides into.

Figure 2.62.   Pushing in process.

Figure 2.63.   Pushing is done.

The model is done, but just to make sure, do the rotation three times (as suggested by Sara Adams). This can have the effect of adjusting small errors in the folding. See Figures 2.64–2.66.

Figure 2.64. Pushing the sides to rotate.

Figure 2.65. Rotating in process.

Figure 2.66. One rotation is done.

Explanations

Focusing on tetrahedrons and the way we folded one provides an opportunity to introduce two beautiful mathematics topics: *Platonic solids* and *tessellations*.

A regular tetrahedron is a special type of solid called a Platonic solid. Platonic solids have the following characteristics:

- A Platonic solid is a *polyhedron*, meaning it is a three dimensional shape with flat surfaces, called faces, that are polygons, meaning two dimensional shapes with straight edges.
- The faces of a Platonic solid are all the same polygon and the polygon is *regular*, meaning all the angles are the same and the edges are the same length. We repeat again: for triangles, the term, equilateral, is often used in place of regular.
- The same number of faces meet at each vertex.

The first model in this chapter has four faces—this makes it a tetrahedron—and the faces are all equilateral triangles, the name for regular triangles and all the same size. Each vertex is the meeting place of three of those triangles. It is, therefore, a Platonic solid. See the Exercises for a challenge.

A *tessellation* is a combination of shapes that can fill up the plane. The phrase "tiles the plane" also is used. We describe the connection of folding a strip of paper into a tetrahedron to tessellations below.

How the strip method works

Here we will describe how the strip method works. Our goal is to show that the triangle that the method has us folding over and over is an equilateral triangle, meaning the sides are all the same length and the three angles are each 60 degrees. If it wasn't an equilateral triangle, it would not be possible to fold it over and over.

Recall the first step of making a tetrahedron out of a strip is folding the strip long side to long side but just making a pinch to mark the halfway mark at the left side.

The next step is to fold the bottom left corner to the halfway mark. Look at the labeled diagram in Figure 2.67. Our goal is to show that the angles ∠FAD, ∠ADF, and ∠AFD are each 60 degrees. Since the angles of a triangle add up to 180 degrees, we just need to show that two of those three are each 60 degrees because then the third must also be 60 degrees.

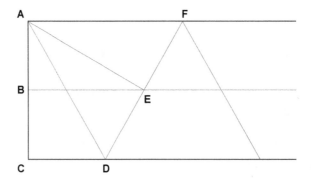

Figure 2.67.   Strip of paper with labels.

The line AE is made by pivoting edge AC so C lies on the halfway line. This is another situation in which are hands are doing the math. In this case, the folding establishes that the two triangles, △ACD and △AED, are essentially the same triangle.

TIP

In geometry, the term *congruent* is used for two triangles for which you can set up a correspondence of angles and sides where corresponding angles are equal and corresponding sides are equal. The term congruent is the formal name for saying two triangles are the same. See Figure 2.68.

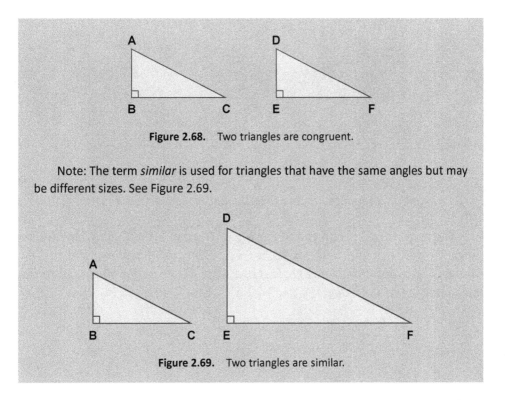

Figure 2.68.   Two triangles are congruent.

Note: The term *similar* is used for triangles that have the same angles but may be different sizes. See Figure 2.69.

Figure 2.69.   Two triangles are similar.

The length of AE is the same as the length of AC. The length of AB is half the length of AC by how we defined the pinch. This means that the length of AB is half of AE. The following equations are true:

$$AB = \frac{1}{2}AC = \frac{1}{2}AE \left(\text{because } AC = AE\right)$$

Now focus on the triangle $\triangle ABE$. It is a right triangle and we want to determine the size of the angle $\angle AEB$. It is 30 degrees because the length of AB is half of AE. (The angles of a right triangle whose ratio of its sides is $1:2:\sqrt{3}$ are 30°, 60° and 90°. These are basic facts from trigonometry. You may go back to Chapter 2 in our first **Origami with Explanations** book or any trigonometry text.) This means that the size of the angle $\angle BAE$ is 60 degrees. See Figure 2.70.

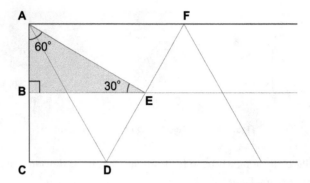

Figure 2.70.   Right triangle with 30, 60, and 90 degrees.

The angle ∠DAE is half of the angle ∠BAE because the folding bisected the angle. This means that ∠BAD is 30 degrees; ∠DAE is 30 degrees; and so ∠EAF also is 30 degrees. Combining angle ∠DAE with ∠EAF, we get 30 plus 30 to conclude that ∠DAF is 60 degrees. See Figure 2.71.

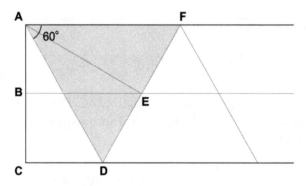

Figure 2.71.   ∠DAF is 60 degrees.

One more angle to go and, in fact, we are almost done. Consider the triangle △AED. It is congruent to △ACD. This means that the angle at E is a right angle (=90°). The triangle △AED is a right triangle with one of the two non-right angles measuring 30 degrees. The other angle, namely ∠ADE, is 60 degrees. The symbol ∠ADE is just another name for the angle denoted by the symbol ∠ADF. This means that the triangle △ADF is an equilateral (regular) triangle. See Figure 2.72.

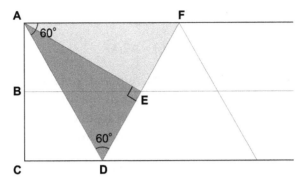

Figure 2.72. ΔADF is equilateral triangle.

The seemingly trivial step of marking the halfway point and then folding the edge by pivoting at one corner to make the other corner hit the halfway pinch is the significant step in producing the equilateral triangle that is rolled over and over to fill up the strip.

Calculation of Edge of Tetrahedron

Looking at Figure 2.73. The edges of the tetrahedron are each equal to the length of AD. Now, at this point, we know that the triangle ΔACD is a right triangle and the angle ∠ADC is 60 degrees.

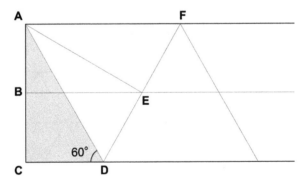

Figure 2.73. ∠ADC is 60 degrees.

Trigonometry defines the ratio of the side OPPOSITE the 60 degree angle over the hypotenuse of the triangle to be sin(60). (When used in an expression or equation, sine is abbreviated to be sin.) The sine of 60 degrees is defined by the expression shown here:

$$sin(60) = AC/AD$$

because AD is equal to AF

$$\sin(60) = AC/AF$$

We know AC because we can measure our strip. (Since we used Legal size paper, 8.5 × 14 and cut it into five strips, for us the value is 8.5/5.) We can look up the value of sin(60). Using algebra, we can produce the following formula for the length of AF, which is the edge of the tetrahedron.

$$AF = AC/\sin(60)$$

TIP

The value of sin(60) is 0.86602540378 using Google on Jeanine's computer. We also know it to be $\sqrt{3}/2$. Since we/you probably do not measure the short side of the strip with the accuracy suggested by all those numbers past the decimal point, we suggest using 0.87. Teachers: *Significant digits* can be a dull topic, but this is an opportunity to discuss it in the context of an application.

Tessellations

The folding procedure for the tetrahedron demonstrates that the equilateral triangles fill up the strip of paper. This attribute indicates that equilateral, also called regular, triangles can *"tile the plane"*, that is, be placed on a plane so that there are no gaps; that is, not just a row, but rows and rows. See Figure 2.74.

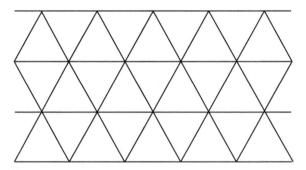

Figure 2.74.   Rows of regular triangles.

Another term for this is *tessellation*. Tessellations can be made using other shapes or combinations of shapes and are the subject of study in mathematics and in origami + mathematics that you can explore. We make one observation about tessellations. Only three regular polygons form tessellations: triangles, squares, and hexagons. See Figure 2.75. How can this be? It is not enough to examine the first few polygons.

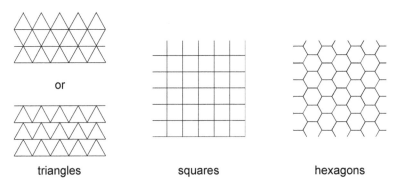

Figure 2.75. Tessellations for triangles, squares, and hexagons.

Here is the reasoning. For polygons of a specific type to tessellate (making the noun into a verb), the vertices must meet. Figure 2.76 shows each of the three tessellations with places where vertices meet circled. Three triangles meet in a row; four squares meet in the plane, that is, multiple rows; and three hexagons meet in the plane.

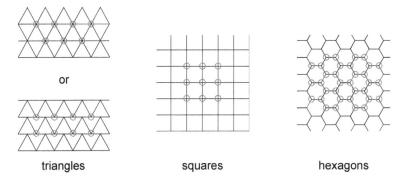

Figure 2.76. Tessellations for triangles, squares, and hexagons indicating where vertices meet circled.

We can think of combining rows of triangles in two ways. If the triangles met at a point, the angles of a regular triangle are 60 degrees each and so the sum of six angles add up to 6 times 60 for 360 degrees. If the vertices in one row meet the bases of the triangles in another row, then the angle for the base is 180 degrees and the angles add up as 180 plus 3 times 60 degrees. See Figure 2.77.

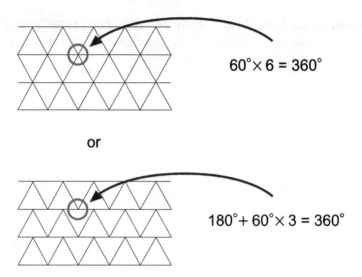

$$60° \times 6 = 360°$$

or

$$180° + 60° \times 3 = 360°$$

Figure 2.77.   Ways of arranging triangles.

Actually, the vertices of the triangles in one row can meet the bases of another row all along the bases. We can think of this as a spectrum. Moreover, pairs of rows can meet in different ways as shown in Figure 2.78.

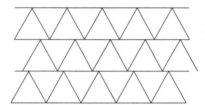

Figure 2.78.   Rows of triangles can be arranged differently.

The angles of a square are 90 degrees each and 4 times 90 also is 360 degrees. The angles of a hexagon are 120 degrees and 3 times 120 is 360. The number 360 is not a coincidence. A tessellation has no gaps so to cover the plane; the angles need to *add up to 360 degrees*. This means that the size of the angles of the regular polygon must be a *factor* of 360. A factor of a number is a number that divides it without a remainder. There is a factor of 360 that is bigger than 120, but it is 180 and 180 degrees corresponds to a straight line and is NOT the size of the angles of any regular polygon. To recap, the list of three regular polygons that tessellate (triangle, square, hexagon) is complete. Tessellations can be made up of other shapes and the Exercises encourage you to explore.

Comparison of Rotating Tetrahedron to Other Modulars

The Rotating Tetrahedron is made up of three pieces of paper, all with the same shape in the final model. In this way, it is not like the Tulip-and-Stem and more like Laura Kruskal's King David Crown. However, it is *not* like the Waterbomb Ornament and other modular designs, including ones you will see later in this book. The individual pieces of paper are not made into units that have a 3D shape BEFORE being attached to each other. Instead, the units have preparation folds, all unfolded, before being layered together to form cylinder-like surface in three dimensions. (This may be termed a two dimensional manifold.) See Figure 2.79.

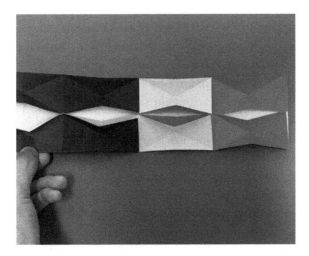

Figure 2.79.   Three units are arranged in 2D.

The model as a whole is then shaped into final form by reinforcing existing creases.

Enhancements and Next Steps

There are other origami models producing tetrahedrons, including modulars. There is considerable activity involving tessellations in the origami world. The next section makes suggestions on topics to explore. In later chapters, you will see more modulars.

Chapter 3 describes the Heart Locket designed by Gay Merrill Gross. The folding procedure will improve your skills at reverse and sink folds as well as your general sense of spatial relations.

Exercises and Explorations

1. Do the research to answer the question: what are the shapes of the pyramids in Egypt?
2. Look up the Platonic solids, especially what they are and why there are only 5. The reasoning for this is similar to our comments on tessellations of regular polygons.
3. Do research on tessellations. Make your own.
4. Origami designers have come up with tessellations, also. Research this topic. In particular, look up Miura designs.
5. Determine the final dimensions of the Rotating Tetrahedrons, specifically the diameter.
6. Angles can be measured in degrees, which is familiar to us and what we are using when we say 90 degrees for a right angle and "a one eighty" for a U-turn. It is what we used in this chapter when we spoke about 360 degrees for the sum of the angles around a point. Degrees were invented and you can research the origins. However, there is an alternative, something called *radians*. You can research radians, which has the advantages of being what is called an intrinsic measurement system. It typically is used in programming. We make this a warning, because if you do look up the sine of 60, say, and the source is expecting radians, it will not return what you expect.
7. Tomoko Fuse is known for her many original boxes. You can find these in her excellent books in Japanese and in English (see Resources) and online.

Chapter 3

Heart Locket

Background

The model for this chapter is the Heart Locket created by Gay Merrill Gross. See Figure 3.1. The instructions will show you when and how to insert a cord. See the Enhancement section for ideas on the use of the locket.

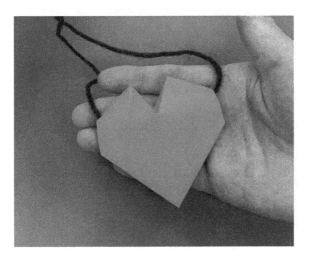

Figure 3.1. Heart Locket with a string.

Instructions

A few hints before starting the instructions: the folding procedure makes use of pinches. It also involves using the same crease but changing the sense of the crease. Some creases are made on two layers of paper and then the crease on one layer is changed. This will be a *reverse fold*, but the reverse operation does not come right after the preparation step.

It is useful to think about the final shape: the top of the heart is built up from the middle of the paper. The model is a clam shell, locked into shape by what we call pockets and pokes or slots and tabs. Our attention moves among these three locations: middle of paper, top of paper, bottom of paper. It provides a real spatial relations workout!

White side up, make a book fold, from bottom to top. See Figure 3.2.

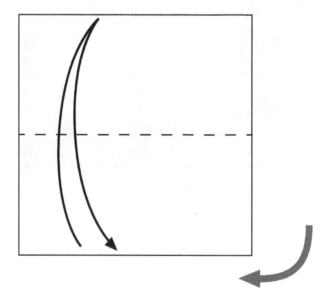

Figure 3.2. Book fold and unfolding it, arrow indicating to rotate the paper a quarter turn.

Unfold. Rotate the paper a quarter turn. Now make a pinch by preparing to fold the paper again, bottom to top, line up the crease lines, but only make a crease in the middle of the paper. See Figure 3.3.

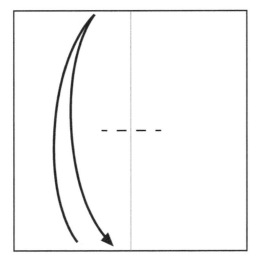

Figure 3.3. Make a pinch in the middle.

You can do this by sliding your finger along the crease line and creasing in the middle.

Use this pinch to make *cupboard folds*. These are folds from the edges to the pinch made in the center. If you orient the paper so the folds are vertical, it resembles a cupboard. See Figure 3.4.

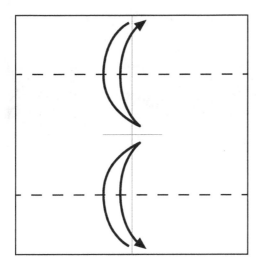

Figure 3.4. Make cupboard folds and unfold them.

Unfold. Now make two more pinches, one above and one below the pinch in the middle. Do this by folding one edge of the paper to the farthest cupboard fold line. Unfold, rotate, and repeat. See Figures 3.5 and 3.6.

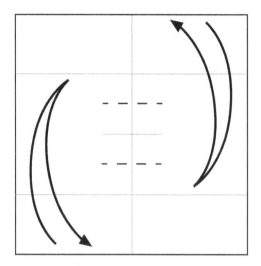

Figure 3.5.   Diagram indicating the positions of pinches.

Figure 3.6.   Making a pinch by folding the bottom edge to the upper cupboard fold line.

Restore the cupboard folds. See Figure 3.7.

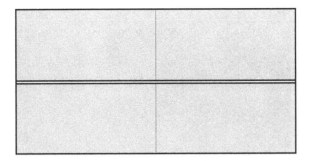

Figure 3.7. Restored cupboard folds.

At each corner, fold half the side to the center line (where the cupboard folds come together). See Figure 3.8.

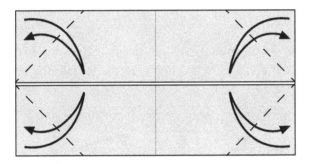

Figure 3.8. Folding all sides to the center line.

Unfold all the corners. Now fold the side at each corner again, but this time to the crease made in the previous folds. See in Figure 3.9.

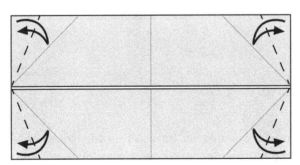

Figure 3.9. Folding all sides to the previous crease lines.

See the result in Figure 3.10.

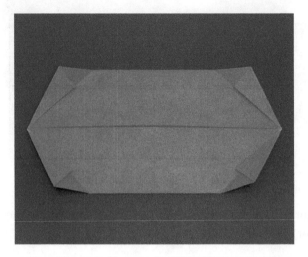

Figure 3.10.   Result of the previous folds at the corners.

Unfold. Now fold the model in half by bringing the left side over on top of the right side. This will be re-using existing creases, though the sense of some will change. See Figure 3.11.

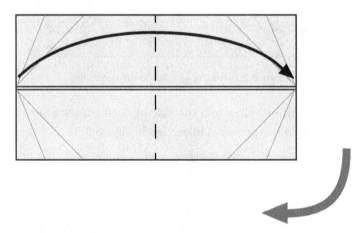

Figure 3.11.   Fold the model in half and rotate the model one quarter turn.

Rotate the model one quarter turn so that the closed end is at the top. The thick arrow on the bottom right indicates a rotation. See Figure 3.12 for a photo showing the model.

Figure 3.12. Model after folding in half and quarter turn.

What is now the top of the model will be the top of the heart? Later, we will unfold to construct the pockets and pokes for the locking mechanism.

Fold each of the top corners on each side so the outer sections of the top edge line up with the closest pinch mark. See the diagram in Figure 3.13 and the result is in Figure 3.14.

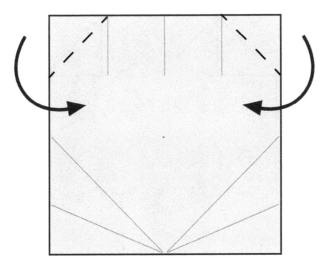

Figure 3.13. Folding the corners to the closest pinch marks.

Figure 3.14.   Result of the previous folds.

You have produced a small triangle on each side. Figure 3.15 shows what the next step is to be. Each of these two small valley folds is made by taking the top edge and making it line up with the vertical side of the nearest small triangle. You only crease the paper from the top to the middle pinch mark. Look at the diagram and then at the photo in Figure 3.16.

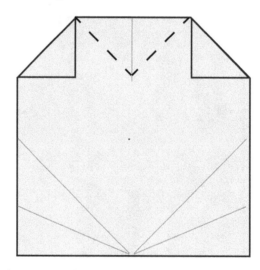

Figure 3.15.   Folding the small valley folds to make a triangle in the middle of the top.

Figure 3.16. Result of the previous folds-small triangle in the middle.

Now unfold the two triangles at the top left and right corners. The next set of steps is to fold the sides to the crease made when forming the two triangles. See Figures 3.17 and 3.18. What you need to fold is four-layers thick.

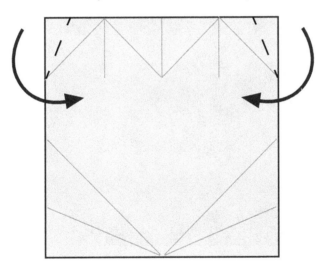

Figure 3.17. Folding the sides to the crease made when forming the two triangles.

Figure 3.18.   Result of the previous folds—two small triangles at the top corners.

Unfold the folds you just made. Now (as promised) we unfold the model more by lifting the front layer. See Figure 3.19. We will call your attention to this figure later.

Figure 3.19.   Unfolded model with creases.

We have folded many creases, but only the cupboard folds remain in place at this time in the procedure. Focusing on the middle of the paper, working with existing creases, change the folding of four creases as indicated to be valley folds (Figure 3.20). It may be easiest to pick the paper up, turn it over, and make mountain folds on the other side. On that side—the smooth side—we now have a diamond made up of mountain folds in the center of the model (Figure 3.21).

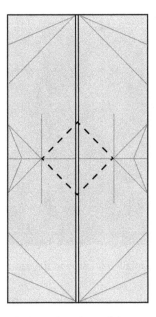

Figure 3.20. Valley folds at the edges of the center diamond shape.

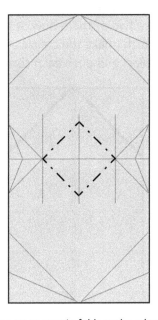

Figure 3.21. Smooth side facing up-mountain folds at the edges of the center diamond shape.

Repeating the previous instruction on smooth side, make mountain folds around the center diamond. See Figure 3.22.

Figure 3.22.   Making mountain folds around the center diamond on smooth side.

The next step is to make reverse folds as indicated at creases that have already been made (look back at Figure 3.8: a step in which four folds were made by folding in the corners). A reverse fold involves making a preparation fold and then pushing some of the paper inside. It changes the sense of some of the crease lines. We only reverse two of them now. A helpful step is to fold the line indicated in bold back and forth (make the crease a mountain and then make it a valley). Then open up the layers and push each corner in. See Figure 3.23.

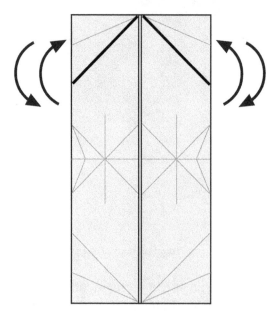

Figure 3.23.   Making preparation folds for reverse folds.

Figures 3.24–3.26 show the process of making one of the reverse folds.

Figure 3.24. Push the edge inside.

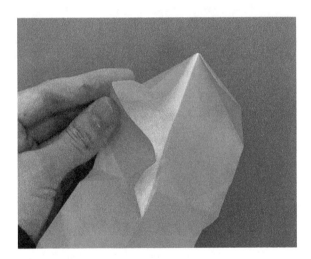

Figure 3.25. One of the reverse fold in process.

Figure 3.26. Done one of the reverse fold in process.

Figure 3.27 shows a photo of the result.

Figure 3.27. Two reverse folds are completed.

Opening up each inner side of the model, there are fold lines forming a triangle inside each reverse fold. Working with two layers, fold this triangle towards you — making a valley fold. Do this on each side. This will be a part of the pocket for the lock. See Figures 3.28 and 3.29 that demonstrate how to make one of the locks.

Figure 3.28. Valley fold to make a lock.

Figure 3.29. One of the locks is completed.

Let the right and left sides fall back into place, hiding what we just did.

Now we move to the bottom of the model to form the pokes (tabs). See Figures 3.30 and 3.31.

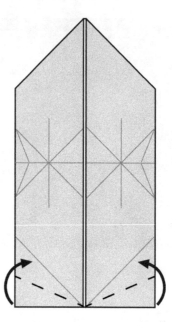

Figure 3.30.   Fold at the bottom creases.

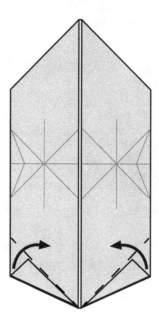

Figure 3.31.   Fold along the edges of the last folds.

Figure 3.32 shows the result of the last two steps and the tabs.

Figure 3.32. Two pokes (tabs) at the bottom.

Now fold (again), the model from top to bottom. See Figure 3.33.

Figure 3.33. Fold the model in half by bringing the top to the bottom.

At what is now the top of the model, make inside reverse folds on each of the side corners. See crease patterns in Figure 3.34 to make the reverse folds. This will be on existing creases.

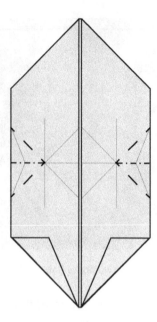

Figure 3.34.   Crease patterns for reverse folds.

Figure 3.35 shows one of the reverse folds and Figure 3.36 shows the model after making the two reverse folds.

Figure 3.35.   One of the reverse folds in process.

Figure 3.36. Model after completing the two reverse folds.

The next step is to make the cleft (the indentation of the middle at the top of the heart). This is done on existing creases. We changed two of the four sides so all were mountain folds on the outside and valley folds on the inside (refer back to Figures 3.19–3.21). See Figure 3.37. Hold both sides of the model and dent the middle with your finger. Reinforce the vertical valley fold that is the cleft of the heart.

dent here

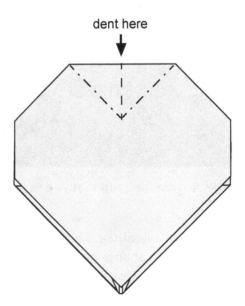

Figure 3.37. Crease patterns to make an indentation at the middle.

Figures 3.38 and 3.39 show how to reinforce the indentation.

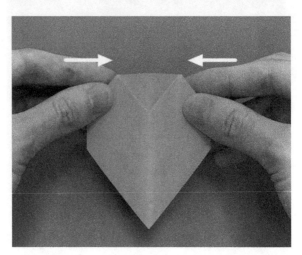

Figure 3.38. Push the model from right and left.

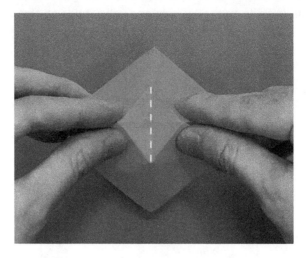

Figure 3.39. See the model from the top. Vertical valley fold in the middle of the center diamond.

Slightly open the model to reveal the interior of the top, lock the inside reverse folds by folding two layers at once on the smaller triangles as shown in Figures 3.40 and 3.41. In the figures, Takashi makes a valley fold to make the lock, but it is possible to lock the reverse folds with a mountain fold as well. Please try both ways and choose the one you like better.

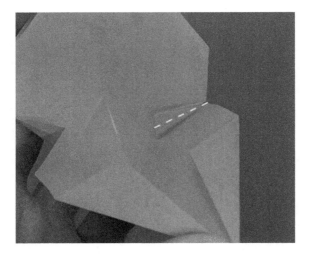

Figure 3.40. Valley fold to make a lock.

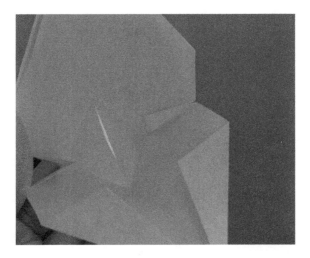

Figure 3.41. The valley fold is done. Now the top right side is locked.

This is the time to put in a ribbon or a message or candy!

Lock the top layer to the bottom layer by folding at the edge of the pokes made in the bottom layer and then put the pokes into the pockets. See Figures 3.42 and 3.43.

Figure 3.42.   Inserting the poke into the pocket.

Figure 3.43.   The two pokes inserted into the pockets.

If the model has indentations, stick a toothpick into the model to push out any dents. See Figure 3.44.

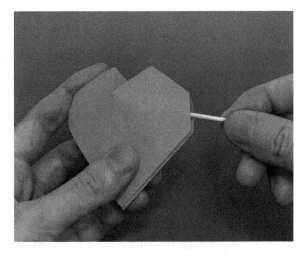

Figure 3.44. Shaping the model with a toothpick.

Final model is shown in Figure 3.45.

Figure 3.45. Final model of Heart Locket.

Explanations

The folding procedure follows the pattern of initial shaping, constructing the parts of the locks and then completing the construction by putting tabs into slots. However, as we have said, the model is a clam shell. This means that while it does have bilateral symmetry, so we do the same thing on the left and right side, we need to think of the model as having three parts: a middle, which turns out to be the top of the heart; and a top part and a bottom part. The top and the bottom are constructed differently after the first few steps in order to be locked together at what will be the bottom of the heart.

The finished model does have a 3D appearance, unlike the model you will see in Chapter 4. The critical step is the making of the cleft by sinking the material into the model.

The pinch marks in the middle of the paper are at what we can measure as the 3/8, 1/2, and 5/8 positions. See Figure 3.46. (Note: our measurements are from the top. Many people prefer to fold from the bottom.) As was done in the Stellated Octahedron in Chapter 3 in **Origami with Explanations**, this is achieved by halving the distance from an edge to 3/4 of the way towards the other end. Half of three-quarters is three-eighths. This is done from each side.

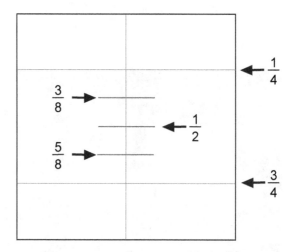

Figure 3.46.   Diagram showing the important distances from the top.

The model has a curved, three dimensional shape. This comes about because of the tension in the paper produced by the indentation made to form the cleft in the heart (see Figure 3.37).

There are times in mathematics and engineering when it is appropriate to provide an estimate or an upper bound as opposed to an exact amount. For the Heart Locket, look back at Figure 3.34. This represents the model when it is flat. The width of the heart is bounded by half the size of the side of the original square piece of paper and the height of the heart is bounded by half the size of the side of the original square piece of paper.

Enhancements and Next Steps

One of the features of this model is the beautiful curved face of the heart. However, if you look closely at the top of the heart, you may notice the two pinches that were made to serve as landmarks at the beginning of the model show up in the final model. We can ask if there a way of making model without those pinches; or rather, can those landmarks be formed in another way. Here is an alternate folding sequence that achieves the same final result but hides the landmarks on the inside of the model, creating a cleaner, smoother final model.

First—what were those pinch marks landmarks for? Recall the two steps that use the landmarks: first for folding in the corners, and then folding the middle v of the lines. So, the alternative folding sequence has to give landmarks for these steps. See Figure 3.47.

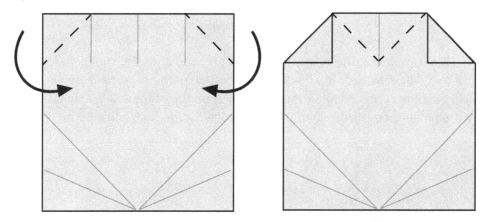

Figure 3.47.   Diagrams of the steps using the three landmarks.

The original landmark pinches were at the 3/8 portion of the page (Figure 3.48).

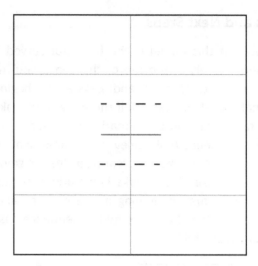

Figure 3.48. Original landmark positions.

But if you note, these landmarks are only used after the cupboard folds are put in. What if instead, you mark the 1/8 portion of the page, because when you fold over the cupboard folds, the 1/8 line lies on top of the 3/8 line, but on what will ultimately be the inside of the model. See Figures 3.49 and 3.50.

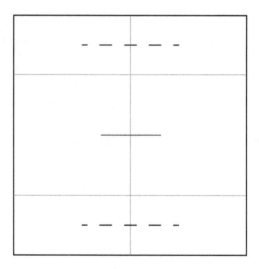

Figure 3.49. Marks 1/8 away from top and bottom.

Figure 3.50. Marks lying on top of the 3/8 lines.

Now using these as landmarks, you can very carefully fold a series of partial diagonal folds to achieve the same lines as folding the corners in and the V fold from the original sequence (Figure 3.51). You'll notice from the images that the "pinches" here are actually longer than typical pinches (in fact they are more than 1/4 the paper side). This is useful for seeing the landmarks, but is okay because, again, these creases are hidden on the inside of the model. Looking at Figure 3.52, you'll see that the diagonal fold can be done by bringing the right end of the paper 90 degrees up, matching the vertical middle line of the paper with the horizontal 1/8 pinch, and creasing the paper only until the halfway point (indicated). The halfway point is not technically visible on the side of the paper you are looking at (although you'll notice it is showing through in this image), but it is possible to tell by feeling where the paper splits.

Figure 3.51.   One of the partial diagonal folds.

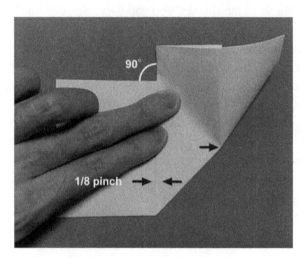

Figure 3.52.   How to fold the partial diagonal fold.

Repeat this fold three more times to get two X's as shown in Figure 3.53. You will notice that each fold generates more landmarks that can be used to check the next fold. You will also notice that unlike the other folding sequence, where you needed to change the sense of half the folds from mountains to valleys, all the folds here are folded in the direction needed. You can now proceed with folding the model from Figure 3.23.

Figure 3.53. Two X's after making the four partial diagonal folds.

You can make the locket into something to wear by inserting a string or ribbon or chain. See Figures 3.54 and 3.55.

Figure 3.54. Put a string in the model.

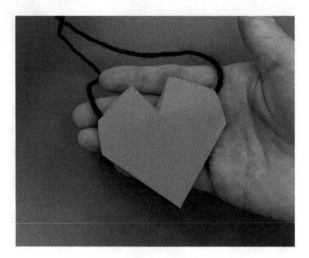

Figure 3.55.   Wearable Heart Locket.

The model can hold a note, gift or candy. Covered chocolates are a possibility.

Experiment with different paper. Foil is possible, though you need to be careful. As Michael Shall and Mark Kennedy, both master teachers and folders, often said, "Foil remembers."

Chapters 4 and 5 feature dollar bill models. Chapter 4 explains the *One Dollar Shirt.* The construction resembles the folding for the Heart Locket in that two ends of the paper come together. The chapter also includes another heart: *Broken Heart that can be Mended.*

Exercises and Explorations

1. There are many origami hearts, including ones that can hold messages, or heart-shaped additions to boxes and other models. Investigate in books and online to learn how to fold them. How are the hearts the same and how are they different? To put it another way, perhaps too philosophical and abstract, what are the critical characteristics that make a model a heart?
2. The folding procedure for this model can be described as jumping around from different places in the model. Look it over carefully to see if you can determine why this is done.
3. The folding procedure includes three sets of steps that (1) prepare for making inside reverse folds, (2) make the inside reverse, and (3) make an additional step that locks the fold in place. As suggested in the previous exercise, these

steps may not be done all together. Identify the steps in the instructions and locate the results in the final model.

4. As an exercise in geometry, how would you define a heart in terms of equations? Hint: one way is to consider it the combination of overlapping circles and polygons.
5. Compare the making of the cleft of the heart (the diamond) and the sink fold described for the Kissy Fish.
6. What other models have landmarks that are "hidden"? What other models have landmarks that are visible? Can you find a way to hide them?

Chapter 4

One-Dollar Shirt and Dollar Bill Heart

Background

The models for this chapter are two paper money models. The first is a traditional standby, the One-Dollar Shirt. It can be the answer to the question: do you want a one-dollar shirt? Perhaps using a larger denomination, it can be left as a tip. See Figure 4.1.

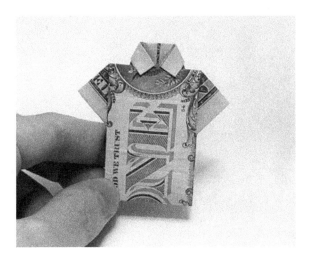

Figure 4.1. One-Dollar Shirt.

The second is Robert Neale's Dollar Bill Broken-Heart-that-Can-Be-Mended. There is a similar heart made from square paper by Edwin Young. Figure 4.2 shows one configuration.

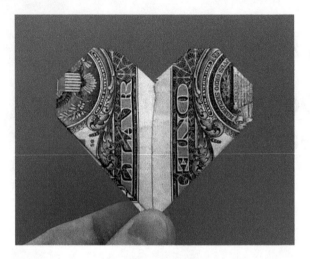

Figure 4.2. Broken-Heart-that-Can-Be-Mended, one configuration.

The model has two configurations. Figure 4.3 shows the heart breaking.

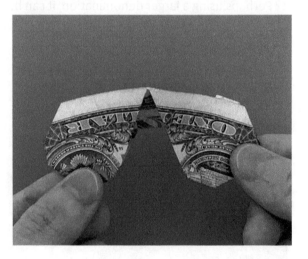

Figure 4.3. Broken-Heart-that-Can-Be-Mended, heart breaking.

Figure 4.4 shows the changed configuration.

Figure 4.4. Broken-Heart-that-Can-Be-Mended, another configuration.

SUPPLIES

One-Dollar Shirt & Dollar Bill Heart

These models each require crisp dollar bills. You can purchase fake money made from paper, even large fake money, which is useful for practice models. The fake paper money is crisper, but not quite as stiff as actual currency. Paper currency from other countries generally works, though on a recent trip to the United Kingdom, we found that the lowest denomination of pound had a plastic portion that was troublesome for folding.

Instructions

Dollar Shirt

Start with a dollar bill. See Figure 4.5.

Figure 4.5.   A dollar bill.

Some of the folds are "to taste" or can be made more exact by referring to points on the dollar bill itself. Fold the left end towards the middle as shown in Figure 4.6.

Figure 4.6.   Left edge towards the middle.

Now make fold the bottom edge to the top edge, making a pinch as shown in Figures 4.7 and 4.8.

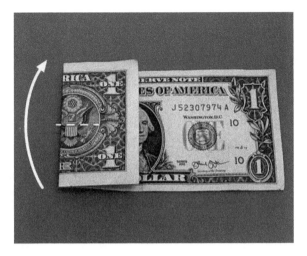

Figure 4.7. Making a pinch by folding the bottom to the top.

Figure 4.8. Pinch mark at the middle of the folded edge.

Use the pinch mark to make cupboard folds: bottom edge to middle and top edge to middle. See Figures 4.9 and 4.10.

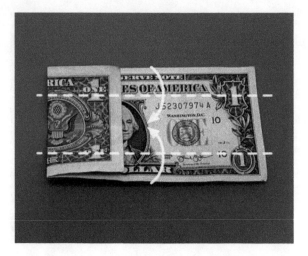

Figure 4.9.   Cupboard folds by using the pinch.

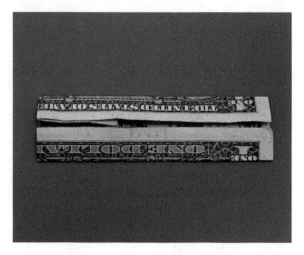

Figure 4.10.   Result of the cupboard folds.

Next, make diagonal folds as shown. Under the cupboard folds, there is a rectangle made by the first fold on the left. Each diagonal line starts from top or bottom corner of the rectangle and ends at the middle of the right edge. See Figures 4.11 and 4.12.

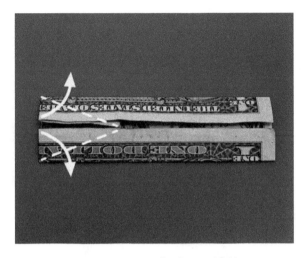

Figure 4.11. Lines for diagonal folds.

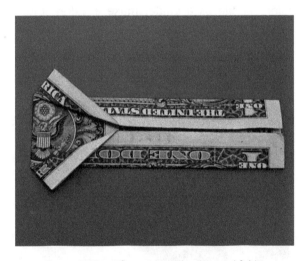

Figure 4.12. After making the diagonal folds.

This will make sleeves on the other side. Turn the model over to see this in Figure 4.13.

Figure 4.13.   Model with sleeves.

Using the color change as a guide, make a valley fold. See Figures 4.14 and 4.15.

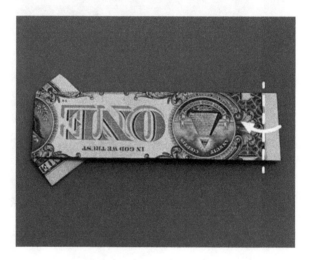

Figure 4.14.   Valley fold at the color change.

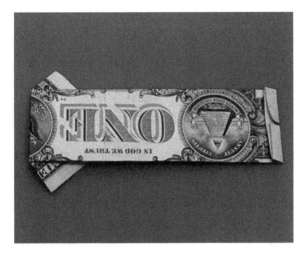

Figure 4.15. Result of the valley fold.

Turn the model back and fold in the two points to make a collar as shown in Figures 4.16 and 4.17.

Figure 4.16. Valley folds to make a collar.

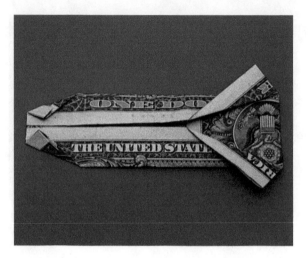

Figure 4.17. A collar is made.

Complete the model by folding the right side over and tuck it under the points of the collar. See Figures 4.18–4.20.

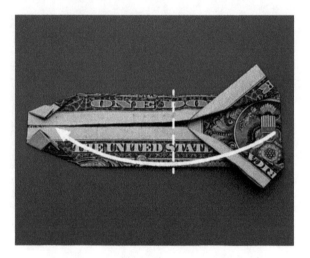

Figure 4.18. Fold the right side over to the left.

Figure 4.19. Arrow indicating how to tuck the right side under the collar.

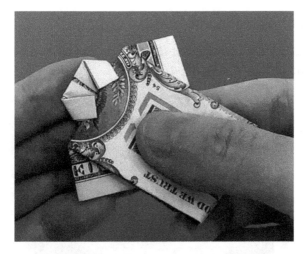

Figure 4.20. Right side tucked under the collar.

You have the one-dollar shirt! See Figure 4.21.

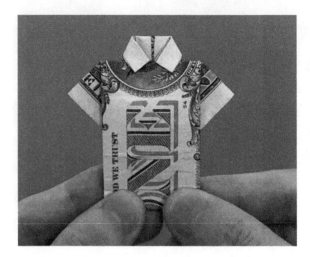

Figure 4.21.   Final model of one-dollar shirt.

Heart-that-Can-Be-Mended

Make a book fold short side to short side and unfold. Make a book fold long side to long side and unfold. See Figure 4.22.

Figure 4.22.   Horizontal and vertical book folds.

You now are going to make a square diamond shape by pivoting at the center of the bottom edge and folding to the center vertical line BUT only creasing half way to the center horizontal line. Figures 4.23 and 4.24 show the first step.

Figure 4.23. Square diamond.

Figure 4.24. First step to make a diamond.

TIP

The crease lines can be difficult to see in a dollar bill (or any busy print design). Consider marking the crease lines in pencil.

Rotate the paper to repeat three more times. Figure 4.25 shows the result: a square-shaped diamond.

Figure 4.25.   Crease lines making a diamond shape.

Turn the model over. Figure 4.26 shows the square diamond with mountain fold sides.

Figure 4.26.   Square diamond with mountain fold sides.

You now will make a narrower diamond by pivoting on the center of each edge and folding half the edge to the crease line just made on the other side of the center line. We use diagrams with photos to show the folds better. See Figures 4.27 and 4.28 showing the first fold.

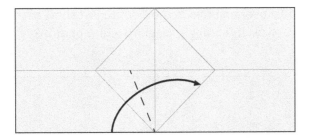

Figure 4.27. First step to make a narrower diamond shape.

Figure 4.28. Folding a narrower diamond shape.

Repeat this fold three times to form the narrower diamond. The result is shown in Figure 4.29, with the sense of the creases. The outer diamond (the square) sides are mountain folds and the inner diamond sides are valley folds.

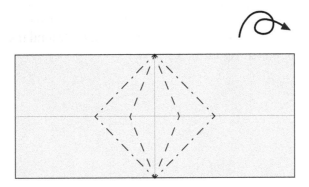

Figure 4.29. Sense of the creases of the two diamond shapes and arrow indicating to turn over the model.

Turn the model over and fold in the sides to just short of the outermost diamond. We again show this using a diagram and a photo. See Figures 4.30 and 4.31.

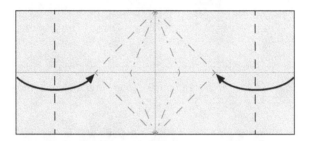

Figure 4.30.   Fold the sides to the outer diamond.

Figure 4.31.   Fold short sides.

Next, we are going to collapse the model. We can achieve this by bringing both ends downwards to reinforce the mountain folds around the inner diamond. The procedure is shown Figures 4.32–4.34.

Figure 4.32.   Start collapsing.

Figure 4.33.   Collapse in process, reinforced inner diamond.

Figure 4.34.   Result of the collapse.

Figure 4.35 shows one configuration.

Figure 4.35.   One configuration of the model.

You can break the heart and mend it by pulling it apart as shown in Figures 4.36 and 4.37.

Figure 4.36. Start breaking.

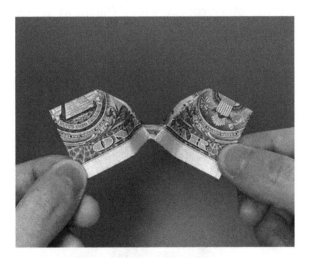

Figure 4.37. Breaking in process.

And then push down the middle of the inner diamond to complete the collapse as shown in Figure 4.38.

Figure 4.38.   Pushing down the middle of the inner diamond.

Now, we got the other configuration. The heart is upside down when mended. See Figure 4.39.

Figure 4.39.   The other configuration of the model.

The basic mechanism has been completed, but we need to make some modifications so the model—in both configurations—resembles a heart. Such steps can be called cosmetic.

We make these shaping folds on the configuration in Figure 4.35.

The task here is to round off the corners. This is done by reverse folds and, where there are two flaps, making one reverse fold and then tucking the other flap into the reverse fold.

First, make a reverse fold at each top corner of the heart as indicated in Figures 4.40–4.42.

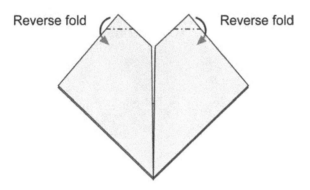

Reverse fold   Reverse fold

Figure 4.40. Reverse fold at the top.

Figure 4.41. Reverse fold in process.

Figure 4.42.   Result of the reverse fold.

Next, make reverse folds at the corners indicated in the diagram. But, just make the folds on one layer not two layers. See Figures 4.43 and 4.44.

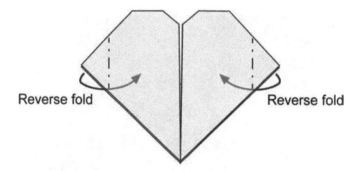

Reverse fold   Reverse fold

Figure 4.43.   Reverse fold on one layer at both sides.

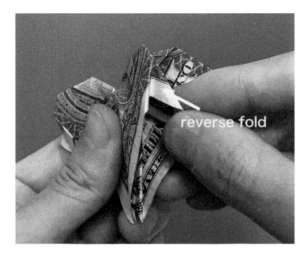

Figure 4.44.   Result of the reverse fold.

Finally, take the other flaps behind and tuck them into the reverse folds just made. See Figures 4.45–4.47.

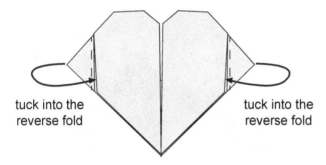

tuck into the
reverse fold

tuck into the
reverse fold

Figure 4.45.   Tuck the flaps into the reverse folds.

Figure 4.46.   Tuck-in in process.

Figure 4.47.   Result of tuck-in.

Here are the final models shown in Figures 4.48 and 4.49.

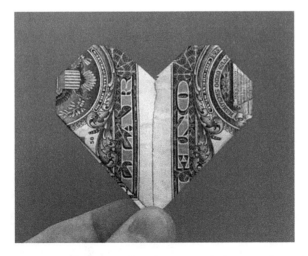

Figure 4.48. Broken-Heart-that-Can-Be-Mended, one configuration.

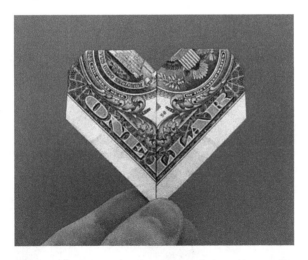

Figure 4.49. Broken-Heart-that-Can-Be-Mended, another configuration.

Explanations

Shirt

The lock of the one-dollar shirt, which is the collar, is made on one side of the bill and then rotated around in space to latch on to the front of the shirt on the other side. Understanding this will keep you from making the collar end up on the wrong side. This is similar to the Heart Locket in that the two ends of the paper come together. Do notice that the cupboard folds are covered up. See Figure 4.50.

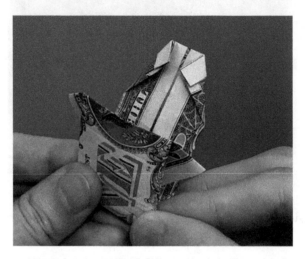

Figure 4.50.   Cupboard folds are covered up by a collar.

The final dimensions of the shirt are dependent on "to taste" folds, so we won't attempt to calculate it.

Broken Heart

The mechanism of the heart consists of two diamonds. See Figure 4.51. (We use origami paper here to better show the crease lines.)

Figure 4.51.   Two diamonds by opening the bottom of the heart.

The breaking and mending consists of the model going back and forth between the outer diamond and a portion of the outer diamond folded under the inner diamond. See Figure 4.52.

Figure 4.52. Going back and forth between the outer and inner diamond.

The angle of the outer, square diamond is made by the step that takes an edge to the center line. Folding an edge to an adjacent edge bisects the angle. This means that the 90 degree angle is halved. See Figure 4.53.

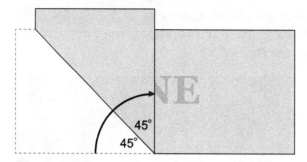

Figure 4.53.   Fold bisecting the 90 degrees.

The angle of the line defining the inner, narrower diamond is made by taking the edge to the line on the other side of the centerline. The angle bisected is 90 degrees plus 45 degrees. See Figure 4.54.

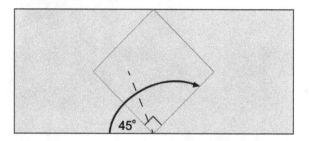

Figure 4.54.   Fold bisecting the 90 degrees plus 45 degrees.

This means that the crease is at one-half of (90 + 45) in comparison to one-half of 90. See Figure 4.55.

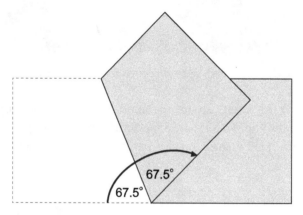

Figure 4.55.   Fold bisecting the 90 degrees plus 45 degrees resulting two 65 degrees.

This is what we want! Just in case you are bothered by the narrower diamond resulting at bigger angles, the issue is what angle is being discussed. It is not the angle from the centerline. See Figure 4.56.

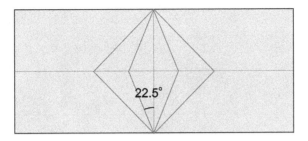

Figure 4.56. 22.5 degrees of the inner diamond.

The inner diamond edges are at 22.5 degrees from the centerline.

The two hearts are not identical. Make one and place it on top of the other to see this.

Another possibly surprising thing is that the finishing steps rounding off the model does indeed finish off both hearts. Do the finishing one step at a time and confirm the corresponding parts. If you like, you can close the book and see if you can figure it out and then look at Figure 4.57.

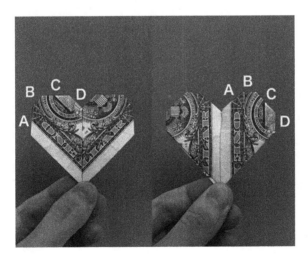

Figure 4.57. Corresponding parts in different configurations.

As is the case with the Shirt, calculating any final dimension for the Heart requires working around the cosmetic steps. Let's calculate the lengths of the sides of the outer square diamond and the inner diamond. Look at the diagram in Figure 4.58.

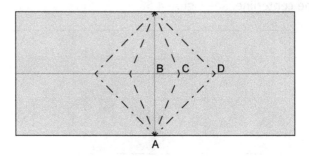

Figure 4.58.   Diamonds with labels.

Our task is to calculate the length of AD for the side of the outer diamond and AC for the side of the inner diamond. AC is the hypotenuse of triangle ABC and AD is the hypotenuse of the triangle ABD. These are each right triangles and we know the angles and also the length of AB.

The length of AB is one-half the length of the short side of the dollar bill. Let's call it 0.5 × S (S represents the length of the short side of the bill). Angle BAD is 45 degrees and angle BAC is 22.5 degrees. So, using trigonometry,

$$\cos 22.5° = \frac{AB}{AC}$$

$$\cos 45° = \frac{AB}{AD}$$

Using algebra to re-arrange each equation to get an expression for the value we want:

$$AC = \frac{AB}{\cos 22.5°}$$

$$AD = \frac{AB}{\cos 45°}$$

Substituting the expression 0.5 × S for AB in each equation, we get

$$AC = \frac{0.5 \times S}{\cos 22.5°}$$

$$AD = \frac{0.5 \times S}{\cos 45°}$$

We won't go any further, except to point out that the cosine of 45 is smaller than the cosine of 22.5 and, therefore, AD by these calculations will be bigger than AC.

Enhancements and Next Steps

There are several models relating to the one-dollar shirt. There is a shirt with necktie and different suits (shirt and pants and shirt and skirt). Going back to paper, there is a shirt box that resembles the dollar bill model. Similarly, there are many hearts, including a paper version of the broken-heart-that-can-be-mended.

The next chapter features another money model, the Dollar Bill Rosette by Martin Kruskal based on a model by Paul Jackson.

Exercises and Explorations

1. If you look online and in books, there are different ways to make the basic dollar bill shirt. Try out several and decide if and when they produce models that are different. You need to make sure you are treating any "to taste" folds in the same way.
2. Investigate the origins of the dimensions of US currency and the paper currency from other countries. Investigate additions made, here and abroad, such as a plastic strip.
3. Calculate other dimensions for the Broken Heart.
4. Describe the differences between the two configurations.
5. See if you can make a broken-heart-that-can-be-mended from a square sheet of paper. Edwin Young designed such a model.

Chapter 5

Dollar Bill Rosette

Background

The model for this chapter is the Dollar Bill Rosette by Martin Kruskal based on a design by Paul Jackson. The Jackson model is made with 16 panels (Figure 5.1). See the exercises for the challenge of doing this model.

Figure 5.1.   Dollar Bill Rosette, 16 panels.

The Kruskal Model is made with 22 panels. See Figure 5.2.

Figure 5.2.   Dollar Bill Rosette, 22 panels.

Jeanine learned the Kruskal model at an origami event organized by Mark Kennedy in Central Park to pass the time while waiting in line for Shakespeare in the Park tickets. It was typical of Mark to organize social activity around origami. He was a master teacher and ambassador of origami and we miss him. As it turns out, the Kruskal model is very interesting mathematically. This will become clear in the Explanations sections. See the Exercises for challenges relating to the Jackson model.

SUPPLIES

The model is made from United States currency. Higher US currencies are possible. Fake money is available from OrigamiUSA and big fake money is available elsewhere. When using actual currency, crisp bills are best and it can help to iron the money.

Instructions

The starting point is to make a *fan fold* (mountain, valley, mountain, etc.) with the designated number of panels. Now you may have figured out that the Kruskal model starts with making 10 valley folds dividing the bill into 11 parts and then, to make the fan, you will make mountain folds in-between the valley folds. The question is how to divide the edge of a bill into 11 parts? The following procedure works and we will discuss how it works as well as something about the number 11 in the Explanations section.

Make an estimate of what would be 1/11 on the long side of a dollar bill and make a pinch. See Figures 5.3 and 5.4.

Figure 5.3. Making a pinch at your estimate of 1/11.

Figure 5.4. Pinch at estimate of 1/11.

This divides the bill into a 1-part region and a 10-part region.

Next, we are going to divide the 10-part section in half by folding to the pinch mark. This divides the bill into a 6-part region (one part plus 5 parts) and a 5-part region. You are moving half of the even part over to the odd part. Make a pinch. See Figures 5.5 and 5.6.

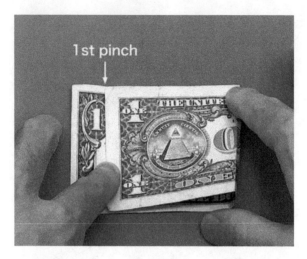

Figure 5.5.   Making a pinch dividing the bill into a 6-part region and a 5-part region.

Figure 5.6.   Pinch dividing the bill into a 6-part region and a 5-part region.

Before continuing, we make the observation that for 11, an odd number, after dividing the bill into two parts, there always will be a region that is an even number of parts with the other part holding an odd number of parts. The folding procedure is to continue this process of halving the even part. The next step, therefore, is to divide the 6-region in half by folding the left edge to the pinch mark just made (Figure 5.7). The bill now has a mark defining a 3-part region and an 8-part region (Figure 5.8).

Figure 5.7. Making a pinch dividing the bill into a 3-part region and a 8-part region.

Figure 5.8. Pinch dividing the bill into a 3-part region and a 8-part region.

The sequence will take you through

1 and 10 (1-part region on the LEFT and 10-part region on the RIGHT)
6 and 5
3 and 8
7 and 4
9 and 2
10 and 1

5 and 6
8 and 3
4 and 7
2 and 9
1 and 10

Note: the folding procedure only requires you to identify the *last pinch* made. We are now back where we started... roughly. The pinch just made is close to the very first one, but, as will be explained in Explanations, it is an improved estimate. See Figure 5.9.

Figure 5.9.   Different position of the first and the last pinches. The last pinch is a more improved estimation.

TIP

Recall from the Kissy Fish model in Chapter 1 ways to mark thirds. One way to divide an edge into thirds is to estimate one-third from one end—let's call it A—by making a pinch and then fold the other end to the pinch, making a pinch at the point two-thirds of the way from A and one-third of the way from the other side. The next step is to fold the A end to the second pinch. This improves the estimate. The difference between thirds and elevenths is only how soon the process took us back to the starting position.

As was the case with thirds, we have a pinch mark at each of the one-eleventh points as shown in Figure 5.10.

Figure 5.10. 10 pinches.

We now repeat the process, but this time making complete, top to bottom, folds instead of pinches. Because the last pinch is the most improved estimate of 1/11, use it as a guide to make the first complete valley fold. See Figure 5.11. You do not need to see all the previous pinch marks.

Figure 5.11. Make a complete valley fold at the estimate of 1/11.

The photo shows the next step of making a complete fold at the 6 and 5 locations. See Figure 5.12.

Figure 5.12.   Make a complete valley fold at the 6 and 5 location.

Figure 5.13 shows the model with 10 dashed lines indicating where the 10 valley folds were made, located at the divisions of 1/11 along the length of the dollar bill.

Figure 5.13.   10 valley folds completed.

Turn the dollar bill over so the folds are mountain folds. See Figure 5.14.

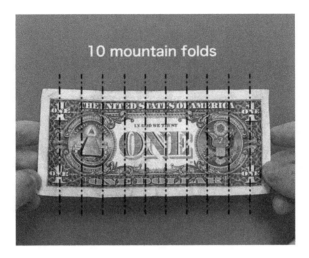

Figure 5.14. 10 mountain folds.

Now, we make a fan by lining up successive mountain folds and making a valley fold in-between as shown in Figure 5.15. New valley folds are indicated as white dashed lines.

Figure 5.15. Making 11 valley folds in-between the mountain folds.

See Figures 5.16 and 5.17 for the first step.

Figure 5.16.   The first valley fold indicated.

Figure 5.17.   See the valley fold from side.

Figure 5.18 shows this step in the middle of the model. Figure 5.19 shows the complete fan, with 22 panels.

Figure 5.18. Step in the middle of the model.

Figure 5.19. All valley folds are completed.

Divide the fan into two. There are actually two possible results. Figures 5.20 and 5.21 show the two possibilities. The first (in Figure 5.20) is the way we want. Notice that the cut edges are at the outside. The second photo is NOT what we want, so if you produce that one, restore the original fan and fold it the opposite way.

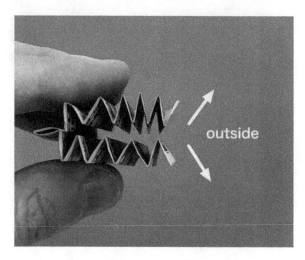

Figure 5.20. Cut edges are at outside (correct).

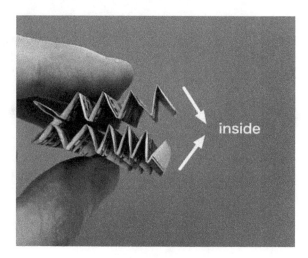

Figure 5.21. Cut edges are at inside (wrong).

Unfold the top panels so there are 3 panels on each side. See Figures 5.22 and 5.23.

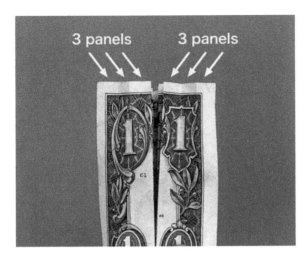

Figure 5.22. 3 panels on each side.

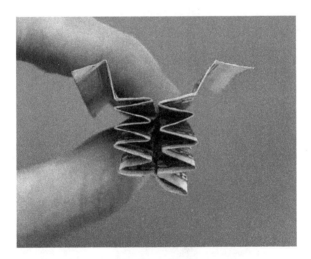

Figure 5.23. See the model from the top.

Now, fold the model in the middle to put the two unfolded parts touching. Note: the scale of the photos will change. See Figure 5.24.

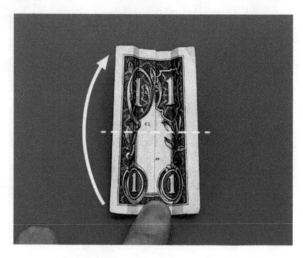

Figure 5.24.   Fold the model in half.

The next step is to make tabs: see Figures 5.25 and 5.26. As we warned you, the scale has changed: we have zoomed in on the model.

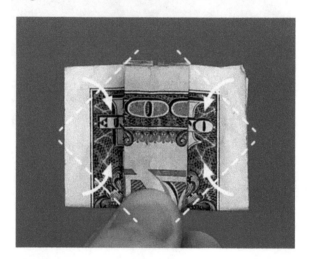

Figure 5.25.   Fold the corners to the closest crease lines.

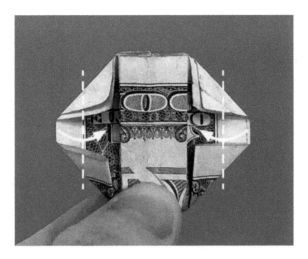

Figure 5.26. Valley folds to make tabs.

Now fold the tabs into the model. See a sequence of photos (Figures 5.27–5.29).

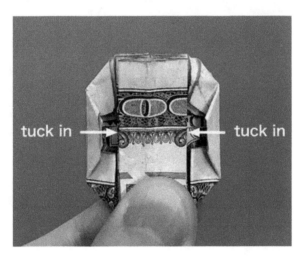

Figure 5.27. Tucking the tabs into the model.

Figure 5.28.   Tucking in process.

Figure 5.29.   Done the tuck-in process at one side.

The model is locked. Unfold and you have the rosette (Figures 5.30–5.32).

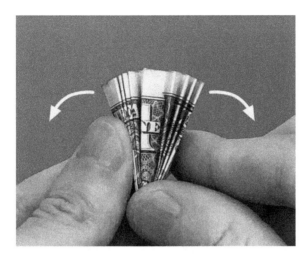

Figure 5.30. Pulling the both sides of the model.

Figure 5.31. Opening the model.

Figure 5.32.   Dollar bill rosette.

Explanations

The procedure to divide an edge into 11 parts is similar, as we have said, to one of the ways shown in the Kissy Fish chapter for dividing an edge into thirds. In that chapter, we suggested making a guess at one-third from one end, marking the guess with a pinch, and then folding the other end to the pinch mark. You observed by doing it AND by looking at algebraic calculations that the amount of the error term—how much the initial estimate was off from the true value—was reduced by half with each step. The same thing occurs in the situation with 11. The error term is halved. Repeating the folding instructions, we started with estimating where 1/11 will be on the long edge of a dollar bill and make a pinch. Then, we divide the 10-part region in half producing 6-part and 5-part regions.

6 and 5

CONTINUE. The next step is to divide the region that is six parts. So, now it is
3 and 8. Then
7 and 4
9 and 2
10 and 1

(We keep going.)

5 and 6

8 and 3

4 and 7

2 and 9

1 and 10.

The procedure has hit each of what we can call partitions: 1, 2, 3, 4, 5, 6, 7, 8, 9, 10. It does not do them in order, but it does hit each one.

The pinch just made will be an improvement over the original guess. How much improvement?

Suppose first estimate is off by error E: Say it should be A, but instead is $A + E$. (Can assume it is on one side). This divides the bill into two parts measuring $A + E$ and Length $- (A + E)$. See Figure 5.33.

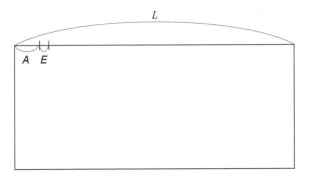

Figure 5.33.   Rectangle with labels.

Assuming that folding a section in half is pretty accurate, the next fold produces a mark at

$$\frac{\text{Length} - (A + E)}{2}$$

from the opposite end. See Figure 5.34.

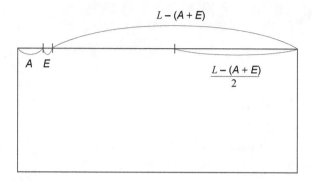

Figure 5.34. Rectangle indicating the calculated length.

Rearranging the terms, this means, and the pinch mark is

$$\frac{\text{Length}-(A+E)}{2}=\frac{\text{Length}-A-E}{2}=\frac{\text{Length}-A}{2}-\frac{E}{2}$$

So this new mark is off by $E/2$ from where we want it to be. The error has been halved! Continuing through the 10 steps, when back to (around) the first mark, the new mark is off by $E/2^{10}$.

The error term E will be halved 10 times. 10 times! This means

$$E\times\frac{1}{2}\times\frac{1}{2}\times\frac{1}{2}\times\frac{1}{2}\times\frac{1}{2}\times\frac{1}{2}\times\frac{1}{2}\times\frac{1}{2}\times\frac{1}{2}\times\frac{1}{2}$$

There is a much better way to write this: 2^{10} means 2 times itself 10 times. The value of this is 1024. (Go ahead and do the multiplication.)

$$E\times\frac{1}{2^{10}}=\frac{E}{1024}$$

In practical terms, this means that this pinch is pretty close to the actual value.

Jeanine enjoyed this model when she first learned how to make it; but, did not think about it much for several years. At one point, however, she asked herself the question: for what numbers beside 11 does the iterative procedure work? By working, we mean that the procedure goes through *all* of the intermediate numbers before coming back to the first step. In the case of 11, all the intermediate numbers appeared like the following.

1 and 10
6 and 5
3 and 8
7 and 4
9 and 2
10 and 1
5 and 6
8 and 3
4 and 7
2 and 9
1 and 10

The procedure requires an odd number so that at each step, there is a region representing an odd number of parts and a region representing an even number of parts.

One guess is that the number must be a **prime**. A factor for a number N is a number that divides N with no remainder. A prime is a number with no factors except for 1 and the number itself. The number 11 is a prime. The number 15 is not prime because it has factors 3 and 5. Thinking like a mathematician, we say, for a number P, suppose P is not prime. This means that P is equal to F * G, F and G each > 1. It can help our intuition if we try an example so let's see what happens with 15. 15 is equal to 3 times 5.

For the procedure to work, the number must be odd. If P is odd, so this means that neither F nor G can be even.

Using 15 as an example and making the assumption the procedure hits intermediate values 1, 2, 3, . . . , 14, if the procedure was at 3 and 12, the procedure would proceed

3 and 12
9 and 6
12 and 3
6 and 9
3 and 12

It would not get past this point and, therefore, not get to 1 and 14. This shows that the folding procedure does not work for 15. We haven't proven the general requirement, but we have helped our intuition.

Returning to the abstract, suppose we had a number P, odd but not prime, and so equal to F * G.

In the rosette procedure, at some point, the pair of numbers is G and (F − 1) * G. In the case of 15, we can use 5 for F and 3 for G. So, 3 and 12 can be understood as 3 and (5 − 1) * 3. What is the next step? The first number G is NOT the even one, so we need to divide the other number (F − 1) * G by 2. See the table below. It may be easier for you to understand how the numbers change by replacing F with 5 and G with 3.

Pair	Number A	Number B
1st pair	G	(F − 1) * G
2nd pair	$G + \dfrac{(F-1) * G}{2}$	$\dfrac{(F-1) * G}{2}$

Therefore, the next pair of numbers must be G + ((F − 1)/2) * G and ((F − 1)/2) * G. Notice that these are both multiples of G. This means that the procedure is not going to get back to 1 and (F * G) − 1. Our reasoning here is copying what we demonstrated using the specific example of 15.

This is making progress towards determining for which numbers the folding procedure works. However, it turns out that the procedure does not work for all primes! To prove this, we just need to find one prime for which the procedure fails. Here is the situation for 17.

1 and 16
9 and 8
13 and 4
15 and 2
16 and 1
8 and 9
4 and 13
2 and 15
1 and 16

Does procedure hit all numbers for 17? Note: there are only 1 + 8 steps. This is not all the intermediate places. The set of numbers for which the rosette folding procedure works is NOT all primes.

Jeanine's next step was to write a program that simulated the rosette folding procedure. She used Python, a programming language that has the uncommon feature of arbitrary precision in integers. This means that the numbers are not rounded off to fit in a fixed size piece of storage in the computer. The program is at the end of this chapter. She invoked this program for numbers up to 1000 and obtained a list of the numbers (up to 1000) for which the rosette folding procedure worked. Here they are:

3 5 11 13 19 29 37 53 59 61 67 83 101 107 131 139 149 163 173 179 181 197 211 227 269 293 317 347 349 373 379 389 419 421 443 461 467 491 509 523 541 547 557 563 587 613 619 653 659 661 677 701 709 757 773 787 797 821 827 829 853 859 877 883 907 941 947

Jeanine was not confident that the next step would produce anything of interest, but she put this string of numbers into the Google search bar and got a hit: https://en.wikipedia.org/wiki/Full_reptend_prime.

It turns out that the numbers that work for the folding procedure appear to be *the Full Reptend Primes Base 2*. That is, the folding procedure and the Reptend Primes Base 2 agree at least up to 1000.

These Reptend numbers are defined as

A prime number P for which 2 raised to the power N, N going from 0 to P–2, produces the numbers 1 to P–1, modulo P, is a reptend prime base 2.

The Reptend numbers are defined also using a process, involving raising numbers to powers and also performing the modulo operation. The *modulo* operation, generally abbreviated as *mod*, defines two numbers as equal mod(P) if they differ by a multiple of P. This sometimes is described as clock arithmetic when the number is 12. Think of going around a clock and counting up to the number. What counts is where you end up.

Here are some more examples:

8 and 2 are equal mod 6. They differ by 6.

95 and 5 are equal mod 10. They differ by 90, which is 9 times 10.

Another way to express those two numbers A and B being equal mod(P) is that

$$A = B + m \times P$$

where m is an integer.

Note that when doing mod(P) operations, the results are numbers 0 to P − 1. Note also that the Reptend process starts with 0 and stops with P − 1.

We demonstrate this process using 11:

2^0 is $1 = 1 \bmod(11)$
2^1 is $2 = 2 \bmod(11)$
2^2 is $4 = 4 \bmod(11)$

2^3 is 8 = 8 mod(11)
2^4 is 16 = 5 mod(11) because 16 − 5 is 11
2^5 is 32 = 10 mod(11) because 32 − 10 is 11 x 2
2^6 is 64 = 9 mod(11) because 64 − 9 is 11 x 5
2^7 is 128 = 7 mod(11) because 128 − 7 is 11 x 11
2^8 is 256 = 3 mod(11) because 256 − 3 is 11 x 23
2^9 is 512 = 6 mod(11) because 512 − 6 is 11 x 46
2^{10} is 1024 = 1 mod(11) because 1024 − 1 is 11 x 93

Notice that we have shown the numbers from 0 to P − 1, which takes us back to 1, that is, repeats 1. To produce all the numbers from 1 to P − 1, we (just) needed to raise 2 to the powers 0 to P − 2.

We note that these numbers are all the numbers 1 to 11 − 1. This means that 11 is indeed a Reptend Prime base 2, but there is something more. Look at the order of the numbers: 1, 2, 4, 8, 5, 10, 9, 7, 3, 6, 1. They are the numbers in the folding procedure, but in reverse order.

We know at this point that 11 works for the folding procedure and satisfies the definition of a Reptend Prime Base 2. We also know that the two sets of numbers (Reptend Primes base 2 and numbers valid in the rosette procedure) are the same up to 1000, but something can happen past 1000. We need a proof!

We decided to prove something more than that the two sets of numbers were the same. Proving something more can seem harder, but in this case, it seems easier; that is, we know what to do. Our proof establishes what we observe in the case of 11: each step of the Reptend process is the same as the folding procedure, but in reverse order. To state this somewhat more formally:

If N and P − N are pairs in the reverse folding procedure, then we show that $N = 2^k$ mod P for all k steps starting from 0, for all primes P.

We need to define the reverse folding process. If (F and P − F) goes to (G and P − G) in the normal folding procedure, we need to define F in terms of G.

We could consider cases of if F was odd and if it was even. Instead, consider the following. Either F was halved or P − F was halved. So either F is equal to 2 * G, or P − F is equal to 2 * (P − G). Which one happened?

For example, in the procedure for 11, suppose that we were told that the current pair of numbers is 6 and 5, how do we calculate the previous pair? The solution is to try two things. If we double 6, we get 12, which is more than 11, so it couldn't be correct. If we double 5, we get 10, which is less than 11, so it is correct. The previous pair had the second number be 10 and the first number be 11 − 10, which is 1. Let's try this for 3 and 8. Doubling 3 produces 6, which is less than 11, so will work. The previous pair is 6 and 11 − 6, which is 5. These two examples with actual numbers demonstrate how to simulate reverse folding.

Moving from actual numbers back to the abstract, the solution is to consider if $2 * G$ is greater than P or not. Keep in mind that P is prime so $2 * G$ cannot be equal to P. Also, since the pair of numbers, G and P − G add up to P, one is less than 1/2 of P and one is greater. So doubling one of these numbers will be greater than P and doubling the other will be less.

The method we used is called mathematical induction and is a basic principle in number theory and other branches of mathematics. The procedure is

Initial Case: Prove the theorem for 1 (or an appropriate initial value).
Induction Case: Assume the theorem for k, and prove the theorem for $k + 1$.

If these two cases can be proven for a theorem for whole numbers starting from an initial value, then the theorem is true for all whole numbers starting from the value.

We proceed with our proof.

Initial case: $k = 0$

- Reptend starts with 1 and reverse folding also starts out with 1. $2^0 = 1$, so $2^0 = 1 \bmod P$

Induction step

- Can assume $G = 2^k \bmod P$ meaning $G = 2^k + a * P$
- Two cases: $2 * G < P$ and $2 * G > P$.

Case $2 * G < P$.

$$\text{So } F = 2 * G. \text{ Substituting the expression for G,}$$

$$F = 2 * (2^k + a * P) = 2^{k+1} + 2 * a * P$$

$$\text{so } F = 2^{k+1} \bmod P$$

Case $2 * G > P$

$$F = P - 2 * (P - G)$$

$$F = P - 2 * P + 2 * G$$

$$\text{Rearranging terms } F = 2 * G - P$$

Substituting the expression for G

$$F = 2 * (2^k + a * P) - P$$

$$F = 2^{k+1} + 2 * a * P - P$$

$$F = 2^{k+1} + (2 * a - 1) * P$$

$$F = 2^{k+1} \bmod P$$

To recap: Because both processes yield the same results at each step, numbers either satisfy *both* the reptend AND the folding criteria of hitting all the intermediate points between 1 and P − 1 or fail both.

Martin Kruskal, in addition to being the son of Lillian Oppenheimer and the husband of Laura Kruskal (and father of Clyde Kruskal, a computer scientist now at the University of Maryland and Karen Kruskal, who gave us permission to use the models of their parents and grandmother), was a highly respected mathematician at Princeton University. We are sure he knew what we discovered on our own. We thank him for what we call an origami-inspired adventure in limits and number theory.

Enhancements and Next Steps

As we claimed in the last chapter: there are many dollar bill models!

Do try this, and the Dollar Shirt and the Broken-Heart-that-Can-Be-Mended, with other currencies. We warn you that the new British money has a plastic panel that interferes with making the fan for the Rosette.

Chapter 6 goes back to folding square paper. The topic is the Masu box and lid and Phillip Shen's Basket.

Exercises and Explorations

1. Find directions for the Paul Jackson Dollar Bill Rosette or you can try to figure it out yourself. How do you make a fan fold of 16 panels? Answer: start with 8 valley folds. Now figure out how to make 8 evenly spaced valley folds. You can think back to other models that required making folds at the 1/8 marks. Go to 16 in the same way as indicated here and continue with the rest of the folding.
2. Try making one or both rosettes from paper currency from other countries. What works and what doesn't work and why?

3. Why do you think Martin Kruskal developed a version of the model with 22 panels? Perhaps, he just decided that it would be nice to have more panels. Why would that be? Do you think 32 would work? Give it a try.
4. Make an estimate on how far off your original estimate of 1/11 would be. For example, suppose it would be an inch. Then, after the one cycle through the procedure, what would the error be?

Python Program

The Python program is shown below and is, hopefully, readable. Comments start with #. Indentation matters! It is used to indicate the content of functions and clauses. Many other programming languages use bracketing symbols such as {and}. The function, *tryProcedure*, is invoked with a value N as argument. The variable count keeps track of the number of steps. The variables currentpos and remainder describe the pair of numbers (parts).

```
def tryProcedure(N):
        count = 1 # start with 1 and N − 1
        currentpos = 1
        remainder = N − currentpos
        while True:
                if (isEven(currentpos)): # determine even side
                        currentpos = currentpos//2 # integer div.
                        remainder = N − currentpos
                else:
                        currentpos = currentpos + remainder//2
                        remainder = N − currentpos
                count = count + 1
                if (currentpos==1): #at 1, leave while loop
                        break
        # outside of the while loop
        if (count==N):
                print(" ",N,end="") #This is a good value
        return
```

The operation of integer division, indicated by the //, is important for keeping everything integers. The program prints out only a good number; that is, the numbers that go through N steps before returning to the pair 1 and N − 1.

Chapter 6

Masu Box and Shen Basket

Background

The models for this chapter are the traditional Masu Box with a lid for the box and the Shen Basket designed by Philip Shen. Masu is the Japanese name for a square, wooden box.

The Masu Box is shown in Figure 6.1.

Figure 6.1.   Masu Box with a lid.

The Shen Basket is shown in Figure 6.2.

Figure 6.2. Shen Basket.

The folding procedure for both of these models involve many of the folds being unfolded and then the model formed more-or-less all at once from an essentially flat piece of paper. This is especially true for the Shen Basket.

SUPPLIES

Masu Box & Shen Basket

These models are made from squares and 10–12 inch kami are good for your practice pieces. The Masu box and a lid require two pieces of paper. For follow-up models, consider getting heavier and/or fancier paper. So-called scrapbooking paper can be purchased at craft stores. Do make sure the pieces are square and there aren't any holes and you do not have to strip off what connects the paper to a tablet.

Instructions

Masu Box

Color side up, make a book fold (edge to opposite edge). Unfold, rotate and repeat. Figure 6.3 shows the required folds. Note: the sense of the fold, that is, mountain or valley, is especially important in these models so we often will show it after the fold is complete.

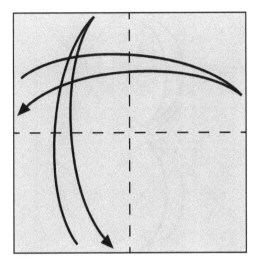

Figure 6.3. Two complete book folds showing the sense of the fold.

Turn model over. Make blintz folds as indicated in Figure 6.4. Blintz folds are folding each of the corners to the center. Notice that you can see the center because it is where the book folds cross. Figure 6.4 shows the book folds as skinny lines.

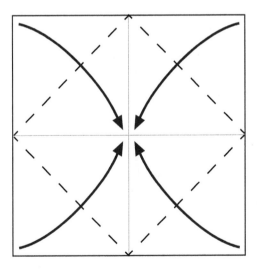

Figure 6.4. Blintz folds.

Now make cupboard folds as indicated in Figure 6.5. The double lines indicate the blintz folds. The dashed lines indicate the valley folds you are about to make.

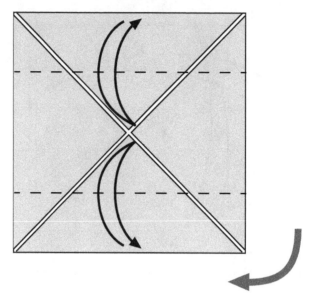

Figure 6.5.   Cupboard folds.

Unfold, rotate, and make cupboard folds again as indicated in Figure 6.6.

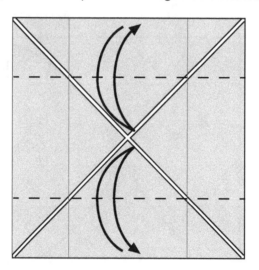

Figure 6.6.   Cupboard folds again.

Unfold the cupboard folds just made and unfold two opposite blintz folds. Figure 6.7 shows the result, with the indication to restore the cupboard folds.

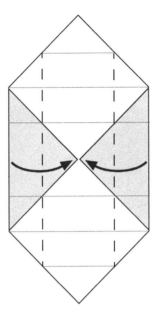

Figure 6.7. Two blintz fold with the indication to restore the cupboard folds.

Crease well and then lift the cupboard folds to be perpendicular to the rest of the model. Figure 6.8 shows the model at this stage lying flat on the table. Figure 6.9 shows the model seen more from one end. The sides are leaning in.

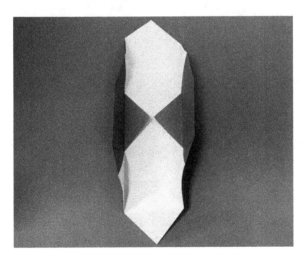

Figure 6.8. Cupboard folds perpendicular to the bottom.

Figure 6.9.   Model seen from the bottom.

Now collapse the model at one end, shown here at the top of the photo. This is done by first pushing in at the ends of the cupboard folds as shown in Figure 6.10. The result is shown in Figure 6.11.

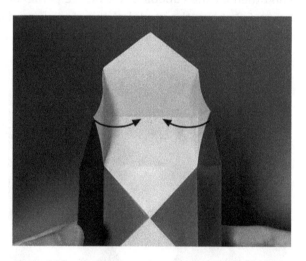

Figure 6.10.   Pushing in at the end of the cupboard folds.

Figure 6.11. Result of the previous folds.

Then, fold the diagonal crease lines indicated in Figure 6.12 to lay on the sides. Figure 6.13 is the result of the folds.

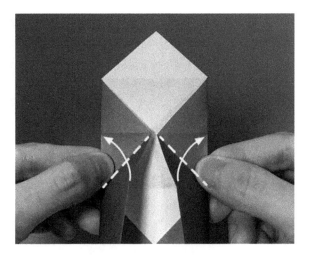

Figure 6.12. Fold the diagonal lines.

Figure 6.13.   Result of the previous folds.

Now make a valley fold at the white dashed line in Figure 6.14 to wrap in the top leftover.

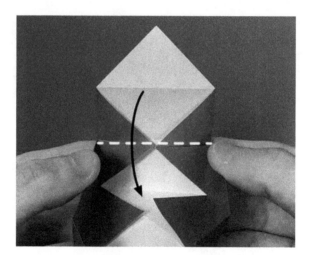

Figure 6.14.   Valley fold line to wrap in the top leftover.

The triangle shown here pointing down needs to be flipped out to lie on the base of the box, next to the other two triangles. See Figure 6.15.

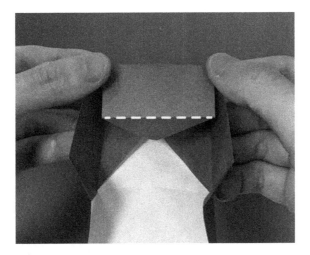

Figure 6.15. Wrapping in process.

Crease well the valley fold made in Figure 6.14 so that the top part is wrapped well as shown in Figure 6.16.

Figure 6.16. Done wrapping.

Rotate the model by 180 degrees (Figure 6.17) and then, repeat the wrapping procedures. Figures 6.18–6.20 show the process of the wrapping.

Figure 6.17.   Model rotated by 180 degrees.

Figure 6.18.   Wrapping in process.

Figure 6.19.   Wrapping in process.

Figure 6.20.   Done wrapping.

This is the Masu Box (Figure 6.21). One thing that helps in visualizing the goal of our folding is to realize that the Masu Box is pretty small as you will find out in the Explanations section. The base of the box is defined by the crease lines closest to the center of the paper.

Figure 6.21.   Masu Box.

Adapting Model to Make Lid

You can make a lid for your Masu Box by making both sets of cupboard folds (both directions) be not quite to the center line. Here is how: Start off for the lid with the same book folds. Turn the model over and make the blintz folds. Now, do the cupboard folds but do not bring the edges all the way to the center. See Figure 6.22.

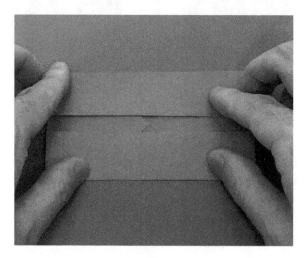

Figure 6.22.   Cupboard folds not quite to the center line.

If you are making a Masu Box from different sizes of paper, the adjustment for a lid is THE SAME. In other words, if you make a top and bottom from 5-inch paper, and then make it from 10-inch paper, you do *not* make the cupboard fold gap for the 10-inch paper lid be twice as large as the one for the 5-inch lid; the gaps will actually be the same. We admit that this may be counterintuitive. Think about it this way: the size of the lid must be wider than the original box. How much wider? The answer is slightly more than two thicknesses of paper on each side. The critical measure for making the lid fit is the thickness of the paper, the third dimension, which is the *same* for different size paper (of the same type)— not the length or width. See Figure 6.23.

Figure 6.23.   Masu Box with a lid.

Shen Basket

We repeat: this basket is one of those models with a lot of folding and unfolding and then coaxing into final shape from a practically flat piece of paper done at the end. Do not be dismayed at all the unfolding. You are making progress with each fold.

Start with a square piece of paper, white side up. We suggest 10-inch kami. When you are ready to make your second model, try fancier kami paper with designs or scrapbooking paper and consider going to even bigger paper.

The model starts off white side up. Make book folds and cupboard folds in the usual way to produce crease lines parallel to edges, as indicated in Figure 6.24. The figure shows the result.

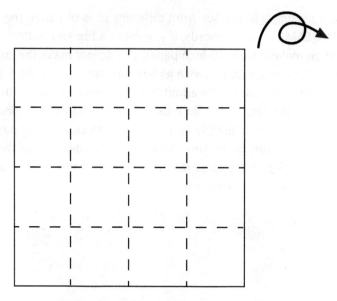

Figure 6.24.   All book folds and cupboard folds.

Flip the paper over. On the color side, make blintz folds: bring each corner vertex to the center point. See Figure 6.25.

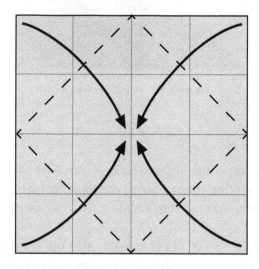

Figure 6.25.   Bring each corner point to the center point to make blintz folds.

Figure 6.26 shows the complete blintz fold.

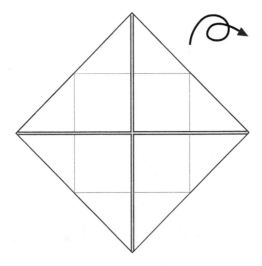

Figure 6.26. Complete blintz folds.

Unfold and turn the model over, that is, back to the white side. Figure 6.27 shows the sense (mountain versus valley) of the prior folds, namely the cupboard and book folds and the blintz. The cupboard folds mark the quarter distance on the paper so we will call them quarter folds. The figure shows the next folds indicated as **bold** valley folds. The next folds are produced by folding each edge to the quarter crease on the opposite side of the center crease. This is similar to what we have done for the Heart Locket in Chapter 3. We made two pinches by using the cupboard fold (quarter crease) lines as guides. See Figure 6.28. Make this fold with all four edges, unfolding after each one.

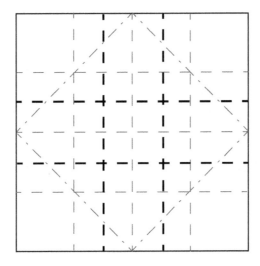

Figure 6.27. The sense of the prior folds and the indication of the next folds.

Figure 6.28.   Folding each edge to the quarter crease on the opposite side of the center crease.

The next set of folds is indicated in Figure 6.29. Fold each corner to the next crease line, which is the crease made by the blintz fold.

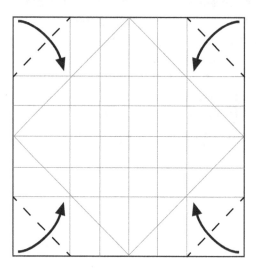

Figure 6.29.   Fold each corner to the next crease line.

The result is shown in Figure 6.30. Keep these folds in place.

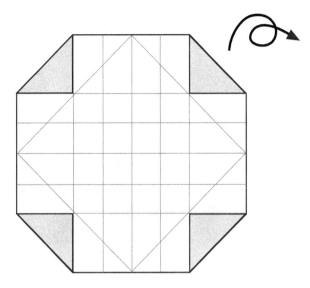

Figure 6.30. Result of the previous folds.

Turnover to the color side. The next folds are *partial* folds: fold the edge to the quarter line crease but just crease the middle sections. See Figure 6.31. Figure 6.32 shows making this fold with the last (4th) edge.

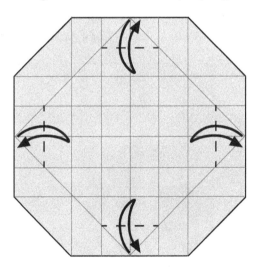

Figure 6.31. Partial folds on the middle sections.

Figure 6.32. Making the partial fold.

The next set of folds are critical in transforming the model from 2D to 3D. We again use a diagram to show what is required and then a photo to show one of the folds being done. See Figure 6.33. Make valley folds (mountain on the color side) from the corners of what will be the base (it is made up of four squares) to the point of the folded corner and unfold. One way to do this is to make diagonal folds—either unfold the corners or visualize where the opposite corners are—*but only* crease the paper as indicated. See Figure 6.34.

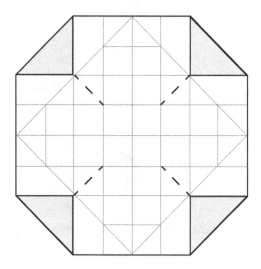

Figure 6.33. Four valley folds for transformation to 3D.

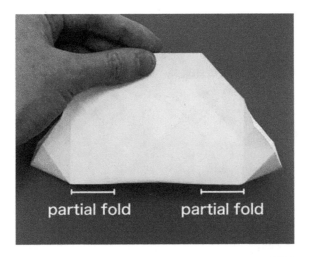

Figure 6.34. Restored diagonal fold to make the partial folds.

See Figure 6.35. We call this the W's. What you are doing is completing a W shape. Make the small valley folds as indicated, and unfold. The locks will be made by folding on these folds to divide the little squares into triangles. Figure 6.36 shows a photo with the complete W marked on one edge.

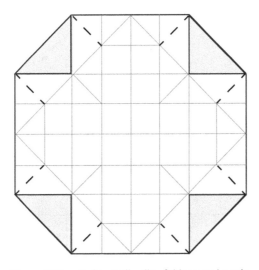

Figure 6.35. Eight small valley folds to make W's.

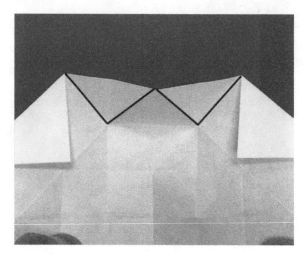

Figure 6.36. Crease lines make W.

Now think of the W's as made up of two triangles. Each triangle divided into two triangles and then is tucked under the corner color triangle. It will involve changing the sense of the side of the little square into a mountain fold. See Figure 6.37. These pairs of folds will be tucked under the flipped over corners and be the locks. See Figure 6.38.

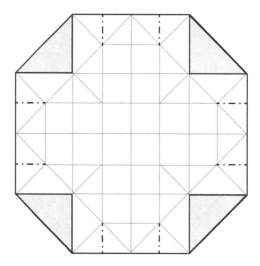

Figure 6.37. Change the sense of the sides of little squares into mountain folds.

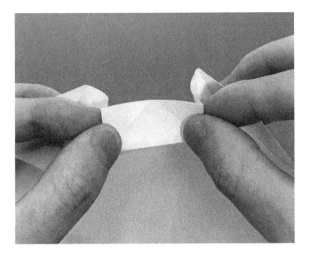

Figure 6.38. Changing the sense of the creases to mountain folds.

Next, reinforce the valley folds at the edges of each corner fold as indicated in Figure 6.39 by the bold dashed lines at the color change. It may be easier to make these reinforcement folds by turning the paper over and reinforcing the folds as mountain folds on the color side. Figure 6.40 shows a photo making these reinforcing folds.

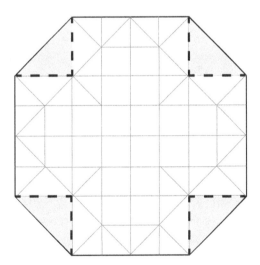

Figure 6.39. Reinforce bold lines.

Figure 6.40.   Reinforcing the existing creases.

Then, reinforce the valley folds indicated as bold dashed lines in Figure 6.41. This will be the base of the basket.

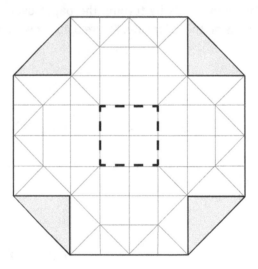

Figure 6.41.   Reinforcing the existing creases around the base.

The last steps, shown next using photos, is to make the model three dimensional and make the locks. What is done is to shape the model, first by reinforcing the diagonals from the corners of the base (the four squares at the center of the paper). The diagonals are indicated as bold dashed lines in Figure 6.42.

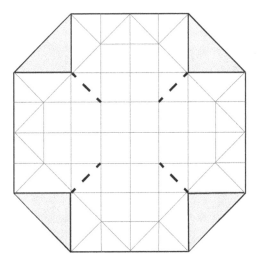

Figure 6.42. Reinforcing the existing partial diagonal creases.

The model becomes three dimensional. See Figure 6.43.

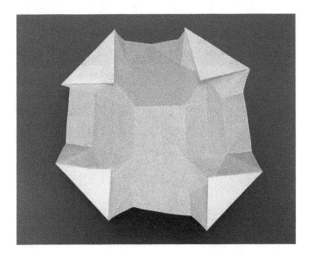

Figure 6.43. Model now is three dimensional.

The next set of steps is to make the locks. Think of the edges as being four squares in between the color change triangles. You will fold the outside squares into triangles by reinforcing the indicated mountain folds (Figure 6.44) and overlapping the two small diagonals as shown in Figures 6.45 and 6.46.

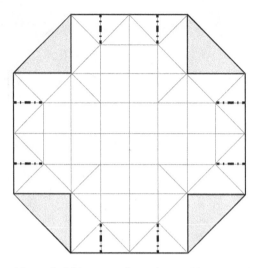

Figure 6.44.   Mountain folds to transform the outside squares into triangles.

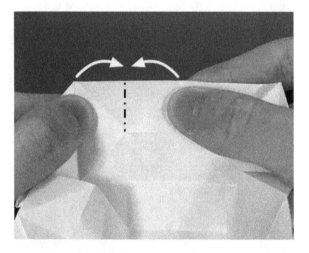

Figure 6.45.   Reinforce the mountain folds to transform the outside squares into triangles.

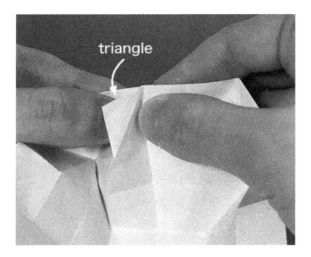

Figure 6.46. Triangle made by the previous fold.

Then reinforce the mountain folds at the bottom of the two small squares indicated in Figure 6.47. The result is shown in Figure 6.48.

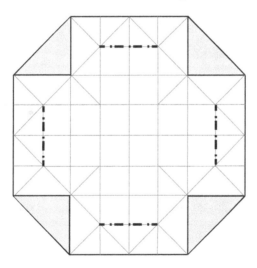

Figure 6.47. Mountain folds to be reinforced.

Figure 6.48.   Result of the previous folds.

Then, tuck them under the corner triangle which has been folded in half as instructed in Figure 6.49.

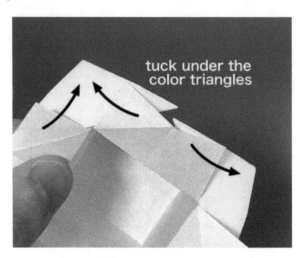

Figure 6.49.   Tucking triangles just made under the corner triangles.

Figures 6.50 and 6.51 show this in process of making one of the locks.

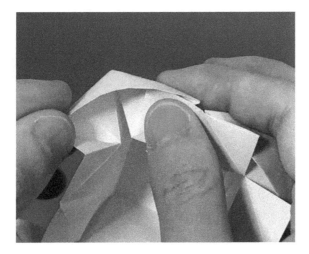

Figure 6.50. The folded triangle is being tuck under the corner color triangle.

Figure 6.51. One lock is completed.

Figure 6.51 shows one corner complete. The locks have been made by tucking parts of two edges into the two sides of a corner. You repeat the same steps to lock all four corners. See Figures 6.52–6.54.

Figure 6.52.   Another lock is completed.

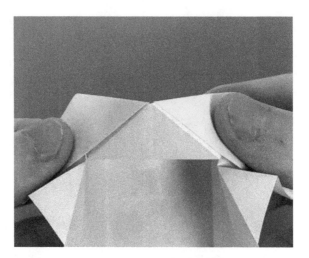

Figure 6.53.   Two locks are completed at one edge.

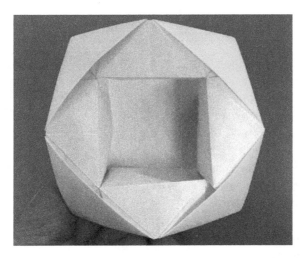

Figure 6.54. All locks are completed.

Figure 6.55 shows the completed model.

Figure 6.55. Shen Basket.

It can be helpful in learning a model to list the steps, possibly in a compressed form using your own terms. Here is our list of steps for the Shen Basket.

LIST OF STEPS FOR SHEN BASKET

- Valley folds on the white side, both dimensions: half, quarter and three-quarter, at 3/8 and 5/8, using book folds, cupboard folds, and folding to the opposite quarter.
- Color side: blintz.
- White side: corners to the blintz crease line. Keep these folded.
- Now partial folds, some new, some reinforcing and some changing sense:
  - Color side: new, partial, edges to quarter lines, just middle two-eighths.
  - White side: new make W folds by folding edge, pivoting at color change.
  - These are two folds at each edge.
  - Color side valley or make on white side using a pinch to make a mountain. (these are folds changing the sense from valley on the white side to mountain.)
  - One-eighth fold at three-eighths in. There are two folds at each edge.
  - Reinforce: on white side at color change around each corner triangle.
  - Reinforce: base made up of the four squares in the center, each 1/8 on a side.
  - New folds: diagonal from corners of base out to point of the corners. (Model is three dimensional)
- Make locks by tucking corners of rectangles at edges into triangular corners: 2×4 locks.

Explanations

Final Dimensions of Masu Box

Unfold your Masu Box and look at the crease pattern as shown in Figure 6.56. The drawn in marks indicate the diagonal and the square base.

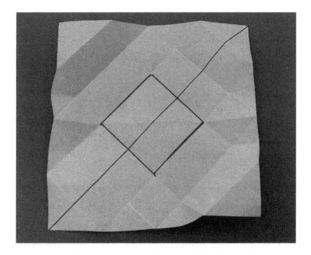

Figure 6.56. Unfolded Masu Box with marks.

Notice that the diagonal is divided into eight even-sized parts. The side of the base of the Masu Box is made up of four squares, each measuring 1/8 of the diagonal. The height of the box measures one-eighth of the diagonal. Note also that the thickness of the box, both vertical sides and base, is double thickness. See Figure 6.57.

Figure 6.57. The side of the box is two-layered (two parts).

We know from previous chapters that the diagonal is the length of the side of the original square, call it S, times the square root of 2. This means that the dimensions (width, length and height) of a Masu Box are

$$S \times \sqrt{2} \times \frac{1}{4} \quad \text{by} \quad S \times \sqrt{2} \times \frac{1}{4} \quad \text{by} \quad S \times \sqrt{2} \times \frac{1}{8}$$

Construction of Creases for Shen Basket

The Shen Basket requires creases at 1/8, 3/8 and 5/8 lengths from the edge. A book fold, edge to opposite edge, makes a crease at the halfway mark. Edges at one quarter length from each side are created by cupboard folds, which are folds to the crease made by a book fold. The 1/8 folds are created by folding an edge to the closest quarter line.

Recall the folding shown in Figure 6.27. The 3/8 folds are made by making a fold to the opposite quarter line. Think of this crease line as being 3/4 from the far edge. Now 3/4 is the same as 6/8 and making a fold to this line halves the distance: half of 6/8 is 3/8. A fold at 3/8 is 5/8 from the opposite side.

NOTE

This technique is described for the Stellated Octahedron in our first book, **Origami with Explanations**.

Peek into Flat-foldability

Mathematicians focus on many features of origami and one is what is termed *flat-foldability*. What are the conditions which must be true if a model can be folded flat at a vertex (meeting point of creases)? Flat-foldability has an intuitive ring to it. Thomas Hull (see Resources) says flat-foldability means that the model can be folded and put between the pages of a book.

Take a square piece of paper and perform the familiar steps: two book folds. That is, fold edge to edge and unfold, rotate the paper, and repeat.

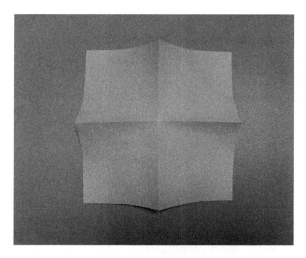

Figure 6.58. Unfolded two book folds.

If you try, you will find that it is impossible to restore all the folds and make the paper lie flat. Opening up the paper, you will observe that at the center point, there are four mountain folds (See Figure 6.58). In contrast, if you make one book fold, and then, with that fold still in place, fold the model in half again, and THEN unfold everything, it is a different situation. As Figure 6.59 shows, there will be three valley folds and one mountain fold and yes, indeed, the paper with those folds can be folded flat.

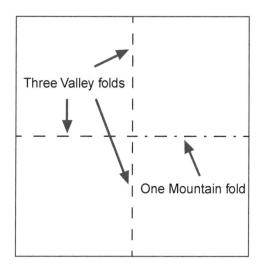

Figure 6.59. Crease pattern after one book fold and, without unfolding, a second book fold.

The Maekawa–Justin Theorem (Jun Maekawa first defined the condition and Jacques Justin proved the theorem formally) states that if the paper is flat foldable at an internal vertex, the difference between the mountain folds and the valley folds must be 2.

Take a square paper and, again, make two book folds the typical way (fold, unfold, rotate, fold, unfold). Now, turn the paper over and put in one, just one, diagonal fold. See Figure 6.60.

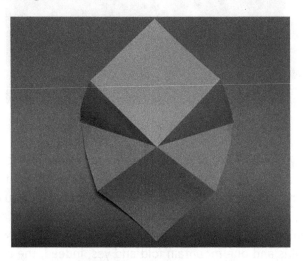

Figure 6.60.   Unfolded two book folds and one diagonal fold.

You can collapse this into a square diamond shape. Notice that there are six crease lines meeting in the center. Four are mountains and two are valleys. Applying the test: 4 − 2 is 2, so the Maekawa condition is satisfied.

Do keep in mind that the theorem applies to folds, not creases. If a fold is made as a landmark or for use later in the folding, and not creased, the crease line is not counted in testing the condition in the theorem.

For example, make two book folds (edge to edge) and *two* diagonal folds (corner to opposite corner), flipping over the paper in-between. Figure 6.61 shows the creases.

Figure 6.61. Crease pattern after making two book folds (edge to edge) and two diagonal folds (corner to opposite corner).

The fold lines intersect forming eight crease lines meeting at the center point. Collapse the model as shown in Figures 6.62–6.64. This is called a *Waterbomb Base*. (If you press down on the center and then collapse the paper, you produce the Preliminary Base.)

Figure 6.62. Start collapsing.

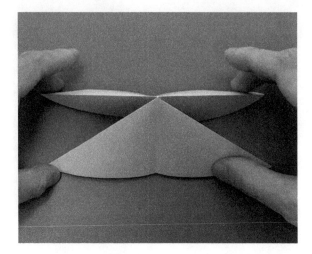

Figure 6.63.   Collapse in process.

Figure 6.64.   Done collapse and waterbomb base.

Notice that the collapsed model, which does indeed lie flat, only uses, that is, re-creases six folds: four mountains and two valleys as shown in Figure 6.65.

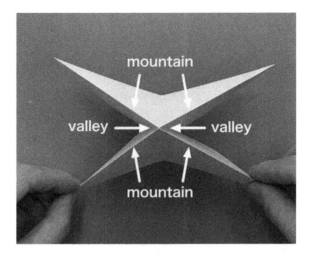

Figure 6.65. Indicate crease types of the six folds.

The center point has four mountain folds and two valley folds and, therefore, does satisfy the theorem.

TIP

The Waterbomb Base along with the Preliminary Base, also known as the Square Base, each represent the starts of many origami models. That is why they are called *bases*. Our first book, **Origami with Explanations,** has many models making use of these and other bases.

The Shen Basket is another example of a model containing vertices that do not satisfy the Maekawa–Justin condition, and, as a consequence, has a 3D shape with (lovely) curves that cannot be folded to collapse. Recall (or think of this when you are folding another basket) what is done to make the model 3D. One of the steps is to reinforce the borders of the square base and the diagonal edges coming out from the corners of the base. Look back at Figure 6.43. Each of the four corners of the square at the middle of the paper has three edges meeting at it: two sides of the square and one diagonal edge. The edges are all mountain folds on the outside and valley folds on the inside. This situation does NOT satisfy the requirement of Maekawa's theorem: say we're talking about the mountain fold side: $3 - 0 = 3$ and 3 does not equal 2! Reinforcing these creases does start the model becoming three dimensional. Your hands are obeying Maekawa!

NOTE

Any number of examples does not prove a theorem, but it can help our intuition. Do research on flat-foldability. An excellent source is Robert Lang's **Twists, Tilings, and Tessellations.** Do not expect to understand everything in one reading.

To give you [even] more of a flavor of the higher mathematics, another theorem, the *Kawasaki–Justin–Husimi's theorem*, states that the alternating sum of the sizes of angles of crease lines coming to a vertex must add up to zero for the vertex to be flat foldable. Putting it another way, the alternate angles must add up to 180 degrees. Note: the sum of all the angles must be 360 degrees. This is what is termed a necessary and sufficient condition. If the angles obey the property, then the vertex is flat-folded. If the vertex is flat-foldable, the crease lines obey this condition. Notice that the theorem does not mention the sense of the folds. It only refers to the crease pattern. Notice also that it does not indicate how to fold the model. It turns out that this is one of a set of problems that is doable, but no one has figured out a way to do it in what is termed a reasonable amount of time. The definition of "reasonable" is quite specific: it means in a number of steps in which the number is only a polynomial expression of the number of creases. It could be an exponential expression. Do try to check out the resources listed and also look online.

Comparison of Two Models

The Masu Box is all right-angles while the Shen Basket expands from the base at angles and the top part seems to be curved.

The models appear to have the same type of symmetry, but the folding procedures are different. Each step of the folding of the Shen Basket maintains symmetry. This is not the case with the Masu Box when two of the blintz folds are unfolded.

Enhancements and Next Steps

There are many Origami boxes. In particular, you can investigate the models of Tomoko Fuse, featured in her books.

Try different types of paper for the Masu Box and Lid and for the Shen Basket.

Can even more folds of the Shen Basket be omitted, or replaced by partial folds?

The next chapter features modular models, featuring the traditional Ninja Star and Paul Jackson's Cube and Stackable Cubes.

Exercises and Explorations

1. Research the origins and uses of a non-origami Masu Box in Japan.
2. Compare the thicknesses—the number of layers—of the Masu Box versus other boxes you can find, such as the Magazine Cover Box in the first chapter of **Origami with Explanations**.
3. Experiment and try on your own to make a Masu variation with copier (non-square) paper. In particular, there are models for chest-of-drawers that involve Masu Box types of folding.
4. Experiment and see if you can replace some of the fold lines in the Shen Basket by partial folds.
5. Read about the flat foldability theorems and experiment with paper.
6. How would you produce creases at 1/16, 3/16, 5/16, and so on? You may have done this to make the Paul Jackson's 16 panel Dollar Bill Rosette.
7. Phillip Shen was a prolific inventor. Do research and learn another of his models.
8. What type of symmetry does each of the models have? Bilateral, radial, etc. What steps in the folding pattern for each maintain symmetry and which (temporarily) depart from it?
9. Miura folding, developed by Japanese astrophysicist Koryo Miura, is a technique of folding a flat sheet into a flat model taking up less area in a way in which the sheet can be expanded and collapsed with relatively little energy. It has been used to transport solar panels and also for transporting devices into the human body. Read about Miura folding and practice making the different models.

Chapter 7

Ninja Star and Stackable Cubes

Background

The models for this chapter are examples of modular origami. Modular Origami, also termed Unit Origami, is a contribution of the modern age of origami.

Our first **Origami with Explanations** book has these examples of modulars: Waterbomb Base Ornament by Robert Neale, King David Crown by Laura Kruskal and the Rotating Tetrahedrons by Tomoko Fuse. The construction of these last two differs from the Waterbomb Base Ornament and the models featured here.

The Ninja Star, a traditional model, is made of two units. The units are mirror-images, also described as displaying *handedness*. The photo in Figure 7.1 does show the Ninja Star about to be thrown. It is an origami version of a weapon.

Figure 7.1.   How to throw the Ninja Star.

The other designs in this chapter are Paul Jackson's Cube and a variation by David Mitchell, named the Columbus Cube, which allows cubes to be stacked to form a tower.

RESOURCES

Go to https://www.youtube.com/watch?v=ScQw_glWYkc for an instructional video by Paul Jackson. Go to David Mitchell's http://www.origamiheaven.com/pdfs/columbus.pdf, for an essay, with history, reason for the name, and diagrams for the cube and a variety of towers.

Figure 7.2 shows a photo of one cube.

Figure 7.2. One Paul Jackson's Cube.

Figure 7.3 shows a stack of three cubes.

Figure 7.3. Stack of three of David Mitchell's Columbus Cubes.

Each cube is made from six simple units. A stackable cube is made with essentially the same unit, but three of the units have an inverted corner, which we will explain.

SUPPLIES

Ninja Star

  The model requires two squares of paper. We used 6-inch kami in our photos. You can use heavier paper, such as construction paper or scrapbooking paper. Smaller is better than larger for these models. Using two different colors is appealing and, also, helpful when making the model.

Paul Jackson's Cube & Stackable Cube

  Each cube requires six squares of paper. We use 6-inch kami. Using three sets of two colors each is appealing and helpful in making a cube. A stack of three stackable cubes would require 3×6 (= 18) squares of paper.

Instructions

Ninja Star

When folding the units for a modular model, you can complete each unit before moving on to the next, or try to do more than one at a time. The advantage of folding a complete unit is that you learn the folding procedure from the repetition of the whole sequence. It also seems more relaxing. However, for this model, we will direct you to start with two squares of paper, side by side, and fold each step on both pieces of paper. This will make it easier to point out where the units are different. You will have a right-handed unit and a left-handed unit. (It is arbitrary which unit we place on the right of our figures and call "right-handed" and which one we place on the left and call "left-handed".) Figures 7.4 and 7.5 show two pieces of paper, white side up, with the first steps indicated. They are the same for both sheets. Book fold, then unfold, and cupboard folds.

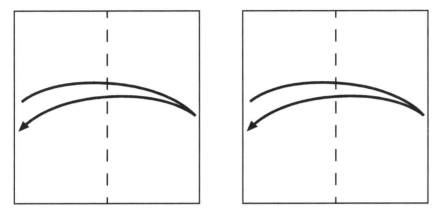

Figure 7.4. Book fold on two pieces of paper.

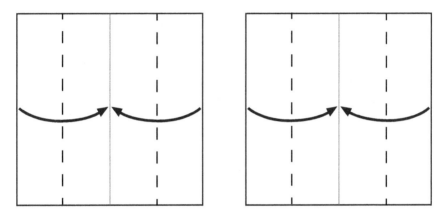

Figure 7.5. Valley folds to make cupboard folds.

The Figure 7.6 shows the result.

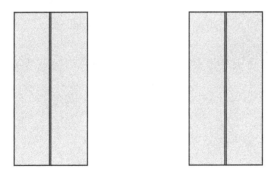

Figure 7.6. After making cupboard folds on both pieces of paper.

The next step is to fold the model in half, vertically. See Figure 7.7.

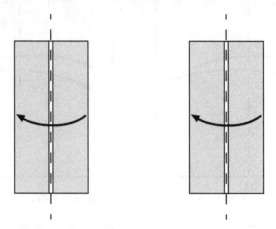

Figure 7.7.   Fold the model in half vertically.

Figure 7.8 shows the result. Notice that the two models are not mirror images at this point. However, the rest of the folding does produce mirror images.

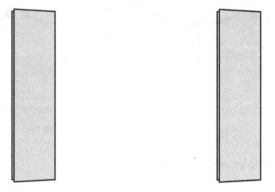

Figure 7.8.   Result of the previous fold.

The next step is to fold the model short side to short side and unfold. See Figure 7.9.

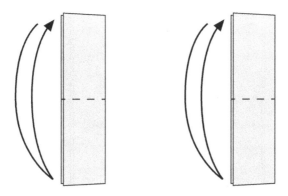

Figure 7.9. Make a crease in the middle of the models.

Figure 7.10 shows the two long, multi-layered models, with a crease line in the middle.

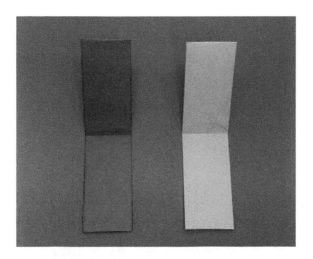

Figure 7.10. Two models, side by side.

Figure 7.11 shows the next set of steps. Fold the short sides to the edges as indicated. On the left piece, the top left corner goes to the right side and the bottom right corner goes to the left side. On the right piece, the top RIGHT corner goes to the left side and the bottom left corner goes to the right side.

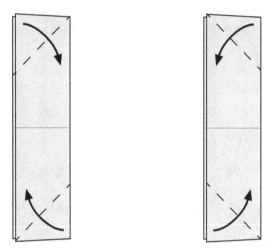

Figure 7.11.   Fold the short sides to the edges as indicated.

Figure 7.12 shows the result.

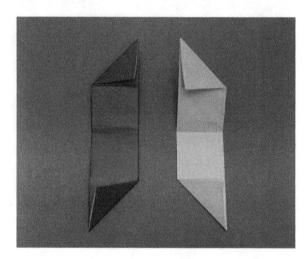

Figure 7.12.   Result of the previous folds.

Now, let's think of the models as being two squares in between two triangles. The next step is making diagonal folds in the small squares. Bring the vertical edge of the square to the crease line in the middle of the models. See Figure 7.13.

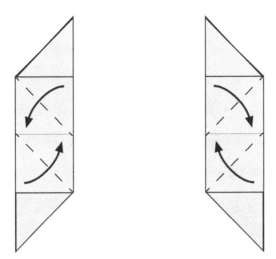

Figure 7.13. Fold indicated valley folds.

The photo shows the results in Figure 7.14. The two partial models are mirror images.

Figure 7.14. Result of the previous folds. They are mirrored images.

The next folds are preparation folds. Fold the triangles over as indicated by the MOUNTAIN fold lines in Figure 7.15.

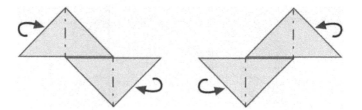

Figure 7.15.   Fold the triangles over as indicated.

Figure 7.16 shows the result.

Figure 7.16.   Result of the previous folds.

Figure 7.17.   Unfolded four preparation folds.

Unfold these four folds (Figure 7.17). They are preparation for the tucking in operations.

The next step is to turn over the left model, rotate the right model by 90 degrees (direction of rotation does not matter here), and place the right one on top of the one on the left. Figure 7.18 shows the results.

Figure 7.18. One part on top of the other part.

The next steps are to refold the preparation folds and tuck the points into the slots. This is done four times: two times on one side of the model. Then turn the model over and repeat. See the next sequence of photos (Figures 7.19–7.23).

Figure 7.19. Indicating where to insert the blue tabs into.

Figure 7.20.   Inserting top blue tab into the pink pocket.

Figure 7.21.   Result of inserting top blue tab into the pink pocket.

Figure 7.22. Inserting bottom blue tab into the pink pocket.

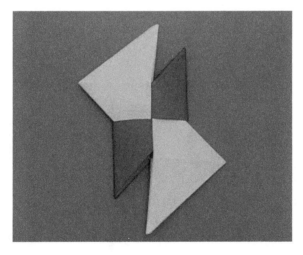

Figure 7.23. Result of inserting two blue tabs.

Turn the model over and repeat the same steps (Figures 7.24–7.27).

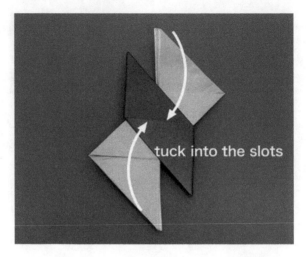

Figure 7.24. Indicating where to insert the pink tabs into.

Figure 7.25. Result of inserting top pink tab into the blue pocket.

Figure 7.26. Inserting bottom pink tab into the blue pocket.

Figure 7.27. Final model of Ninja Star.

The Ninja Star is thrown as indicated in Figure 7.28.

Figure 7.28.   How to throw the Ninja Star.

Jackson Cube

The Jackson Cube requires six units. These correspond to the six faces of a cube. The Waterbomb Ornament, in **Origami with Explanations,** also uses six units. Making the units with three pairs, each pair consisting of two sheets of paper of the same color, helps guide the folding.

To make one unit, start with white side up and make a pinch at the halfway point in each dimension. This is done by starting to make a book fold, but only creasing a small amount at one edge. Unfold. Rotate the paper, and repeat. Figure 7.29 shows the markings.

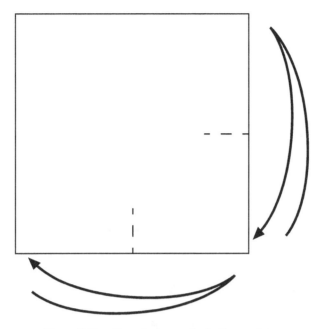

Figure 7.29. Two pinches at the halfway points.

Now use one of the pinches to make cupboard folds. These are complete folds: edge to edge. See Figure 7.30.

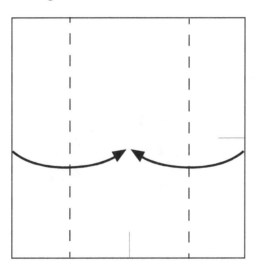

Figure 7.30. Use one of the pinches to make cupboard folds.

Do not unfold! The other pinch should be visible at the center of the model as shown in Figure 7.31.

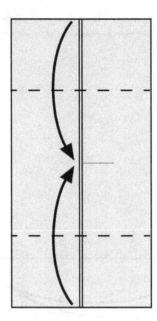

Figure 7.31.   Cupboard folds with a pinch at the center.

Use this pinch, to make cupboard folds. That is, fold the edges to the pinch mark. Figure 7.32 shows the results. Notice that the last folds are facing up. We will call these the tabs. Note: this modular has tabs, but no pockets. The square lying on the table will be an outward facing face of the cube.

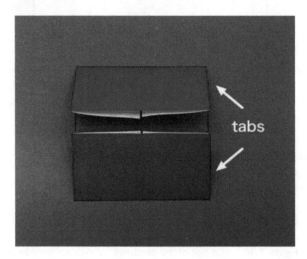

Figure 7.32.   One modular unit with two tabs.

Repeat this for the remaining five sheets. Figure 7.33 shows a good way to arrange the six units.

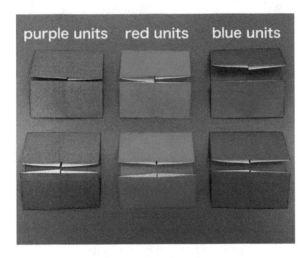

Figure 7.33.   Six units.

Follow along our instructions with the colors you choose. Take one unit of red and place it on the table with the tabs up. There are two sides with tabs and two sides without tabs. Take a blue unit and stand it with one tab on top of a side without a tab. See Figures 7.34 and 7.35.

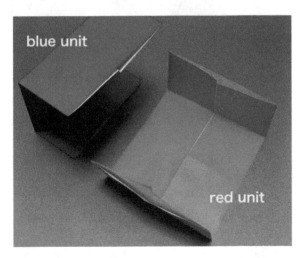

Figure 7.34.   Two units are placed in correct arrangement.

Figure 7.35.   Two units are combined.

Notice that tabs lie inside what will be the outside faces of the model.

Now take the second blue unit and position it facing the first blue unit, standing on one tab, with that tab lying on the red unit, in the place without a tab. See Figure 7.36.

Figure 7.36.   Two blue units are facing each other.

If we describe the red unit as facing up and the blue units facing east and west, the purple units will face north and south. Take a purple unit and position it as shown in Figure 7.37.

Figure 7.37. Purple unit inserted from "north" side.

Continue with the second purple unit. See Figure 7.38.

Figure 7.38. Another purple unit is inserted.

The last unit to put in place is the other red unit. It will be placed on top, pointing towards the other red unit. The second photo shows the finished cube. See Figures 7.39 and 7.40.

Figure 7.39. The last unit (red unit) is inserted.

Figure 7.40. Finished cube.

Observe now that three units come together at each corner. We can use fancier language and call this a vertex. There are 6 faces, 8 vertices and 12 edges.

Stackable Cube (Columbus Cube)

A stackable cube is made by building a cube with one inverted corner. Make six units the regular way. Three of these units will be modified, one of each color assuming you are using three pairs of two sheets each of the same color. The modification is the following. After making the second cupboard folds (see Figure 7.32), fold the right, bottom corner to the center. See Figure 7.41.

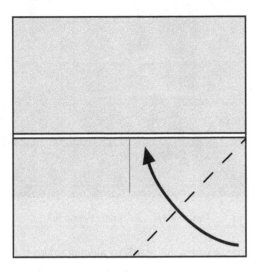

Figure 7.41. Fold a line indicated.

This is a preparation fold for a reverse fold. Unfold the preparation fold and then form the reverse fold by pressing the corner inside. See Figure 7.42 showing how to make the reverse fold and Figure 7.43 for the result.

Figure 7.42. Reverse fold in process.

Figure 7.43.   Finished reverse fold.

Do this for two more units. BE SURE to always make this fold on the bottom, right corner. See photo of three units with the reverse folds in the same position (Figure 7.44).

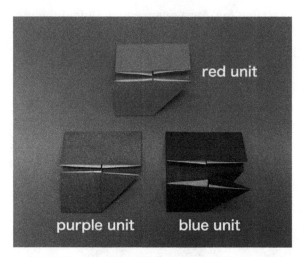

Figure 7.44.   Three units with reverse folds at the bottom right corner.

The stackable cube is put together by putting the three units with inverted corners together first. See Figures 7.45 and 7.46. The placement for the corner follows the same layering as the plain cube. In Figure 7.45, the purple unit is placed on the blue one. At the inverted corner, the purple part comes over the blue part. In Figure 7.46, the red unit is inserted, and at the corner, the red part is over the purple one and the blue part is over the red one.

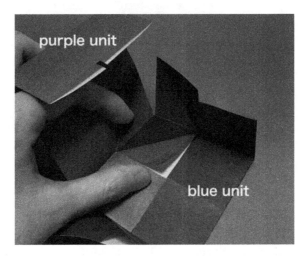

Figure 7.45. Two unit combined together and one reverse fold overlapping another.

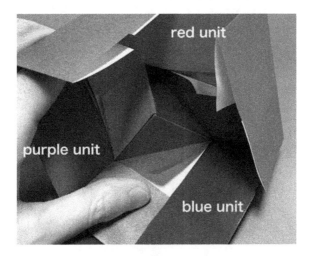

Figure 7.46. Three units coming together.

Figure 7.47.   Result of the three units coming together.

Then proceeding as before. Inserting the remaining three units to form a cube (Figure 7.47). Refer to the directions for the normal cube (the one without inverted corner) to construct the rest parts of the model. Figure 7.48 shows the final model of the *David Mitchell Columbus Cube.*

Figure 7.48.   David Mitchell Columbus Cube.

To make a stack, make two or more models. Place the first one with the inverted corner on the table. Place a second cube on top, fitting the top corner of the first cube (the one on the bottom) into the inverted corner of the second cube (the one on the top). See Figures 7.49 and 7.50.

Figure 7.49. Placing one cube onto the other.

Figure 7.50. A stack of two cubes.

Explanations

The Ninja Star and the single Jackson Cube as well as a stack of cubes are each built by completely formed units. The Ninja Star features pocket-and-poke construction. The cube does not have pockets. We repeat: this model has tabs, also called pokes, but no pockets. It stays together by the pressure of the second cupboard folds in one unit pressing against the sides of the other units.

When it comes to Stackable Cubes (Mitchell's Columbus Cubes), the cubes stack because they do have pockets and pokes. A corner pokes into an inverted corner. A stackable cube stands on a corner because the triangle makes a stable base.

TIP

Yes, the cubes do stack, but if you want to make a tall tower, we recommend the use of a glue gun!

A stack of cubes can be viewed as a second-order modular: a modular made up of modulars. For a stack, the units are cubes! They fit together using the inverted corner as a pocket.

The handedness of both the Ninja Star units and the stackable cube with three of the six units having inverted corners is critical to the construction. Handedness also is termed as mirror-image or chiral. An important way to think about symmetries is to focus on what transformation of all or part of a model at a specific stage will map over to another part or all of the model. A flat model has *bilateral symmetry*, also called mirror symmetry, if you can define a line, termed an axis, and pick up the paper on one side of the axis, rotate it in 3D and lay it on top of the other side. If we put the two Ninja Star units next to each other with the axis in between, then we can pick up one unit, rotate it in space, and lay it on top of the other. See Figure 7.51.

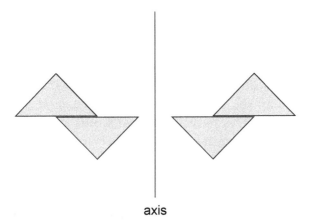

axis

Figure 7.51. Two Ninja Star units bilaterally symmetrical around the axis in between.

The three units of the stackable cube with the inverted corners do not have mirror symmetry. However, these three units are all the same. You can pick up one and place it (translate it) on top of another and have it match. The other three units do have bilateral symmetry.

The final dimension of the Jackson Cube can be determined by examining a unit. The sets of cupboard folds each halve the length of the side of the original paper. The resulting square, which is a face of the final cube, has a side of length half the size of the original square. See Figure 7.52.

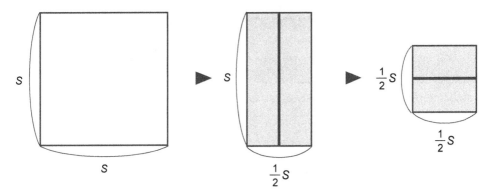

Figure 7.52. Indicating important lengths.

Enhancements and Next Steps

Columbus Towers and other sculptures can be built from the cubes which have more than one corner inverted (although this may lower the stability of the tower in some cases). You can also vary the relative sizes of the cubes and the color scheme of the cubes you use. In addition, towers can be connected together using simple joining pieces to make walls and other more complex sculptural forms. (Go to the links suggested earlier in the chapter and the websites for Paul Jackson and David Mitchell cited in the Resources page.)

Modular or unit origami is one of the innovations of modern origami. It may have started with Toshie Takahama and Mitsunobu Sonobe in Japan in the early 1970s. What is now called the Sonobe unit can be used for a wide variety of models, including Toshie's Jewel. Robert Neale, Kunihiko Kasahara and Lewis Simon also were early pioneers of modular origami. Bennett Arnstein and Rona Gurkewitz took up Lewis Simon's work, publishing several books that present variations of the Sonobe unit, as well as other, original models. They describe systems of modulars. Minako Ishibashi designed several modulars, including one called Japanese Brocade, but also known as the Ishibashi Ball. It is essentially a cube but with extra ornamentation that makes it easier to produce than it looks. Jeannine Mosely is known for her very large structures, for example, what she terms a level-three approximation of the Menger Sponge fractal. She has led workshops where groups of people build structures involving thousands of units. Thomas Hull invented several modular models, including Five Intersecting Tetrahedra. He is an expert on origami mathematics as well as incorporating origami into education.

Chapter 7 is an introduction to what is called Fold and Cut, or, more accurately, Fold and One-Snip. You will learn two models and get a peek into an amazing result of origami mathematics.

Exercises and Explorations

1. How many layers of paper are in each part of the Ninja Star? You can determine this in two ways: keep track during the folding AND take the model apart and count when you are unfolding each piece.
2. How many layers of paper are in the final Jackson Cube?
3. There are versions of the Jackson Cube made with Business Cards. Try to figure out a workable design.
4. Investigate the use of a connecting piece to connect stacks of cubes.

5. Review the modulars you have learned. How are they the same and how are they different? For example, are the units fully formed before being attached to each other? Are the units essentially 2D or 3D?

6. For your general amusement, and for the next exercise, look up fractals, discovered by Benoit Mandelbrot. Gene Stanley has done research and written extensively on fractals in nature.

7. Research the work of Jeannine Mosely and explain why she terms one of her projects "a level-three approximation of the Menger Sponge fractal."

8. Explore other modular models, perhaps the work of the people we have mentioned, or others. Compare with what we have described in this book.

9. Jeanine thought there could be a short cut for the Columbus Cube (the stackable unit): make each unit, including the reverse folds, but unfold the reverse folds. Put the model together in the standard way, making sure to match the corners with the (unfolded) reverse fold. When the cube is complete: press in at the corner. It will look fine. However, Takashi (and Aviva and, eventually, Jeanine) decided that it does not work. Try it and see if you see any problem. Hint: what is and what is not taking place inside at the corners?

Chapter 8

One-Snip 5-Pointed Star and One-Snip Square Letter O

Background

There is a story, mostly likely a myth, that Betsy Ross and George Washington and others met to design the flag for what would be the United States of America. The original idea was to use 6-pointed stars but Betsy Ross suggested using 5-pointed stars. She demonstrated how 5-pointed stars could be produced by making a few simple folds of a piece of cloth and then making one cut with a scissors. The challenge of what is called "fold and cut" has history independent of Betsy Ross, but the 5-pointed star is a famous example. The first model for this chapter is the 5-pointed star, shown in Figure 8.1. The paper on the left is what is left over after the one cut.

Figure 8.1.   Five-pointed star plus leftovers.

It is a challenge to think of how to produce other shapes with folds and just one snip. We set ourselves the task of producing what we call a Square letter O, shown in Figure 8.2.

Figure 8.2.   Square Letter O.

We will show the thought process for producing this shape. The Explanations section describes briefly a relevant and amazing mathematical result by Erik Demaine and others.

Instructions

5-Pointed Star

Take a sheet of 8.5×11 and make a book fold short side to short side. See Figure 8.3.

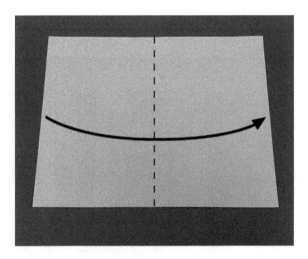

Figure 8.3. A book fold.

Make a pinch mark marking the half-way point on the short edge at the bottom by folding a layer from the cut edges back to the folded edge and unfold (Figure 8.4). Figure 8.5 shows the pinch mark.

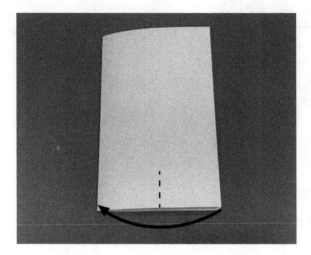

Figure 8.4.   Valley fold to make a pinch.

Figure 8.5.   A pinch at the half-way point (folded edge is on the left side).

Now fold the top left corner, folded edge, down to the pinch mark along the bottom edges (Figure 8.6). Figure 8.7 shows the result.

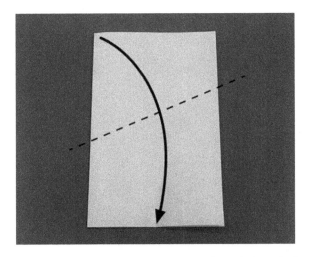

Figure 8.6.   The top left corner comes down to the pink mark along the bottom edges.

Figure 8.7.   Result of the previous fold.

Fold the bottom triangle on the left over the flap just made (Figure 8.8). Figure 8.9 shows the result.

Figure 8.8.   Bottom triangle on the left over the flap.

Figure 8.9.   Result of the previous fold.

Fold the top edge behind (making a mountain fold) to meet the left folded edge (Figure 8.10). The result is shown in Figure 8.11.

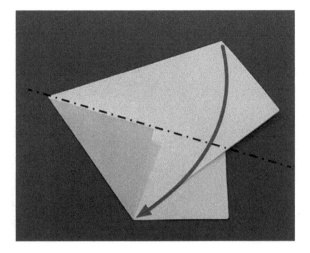

Figure 8.10.   Fold the top edge behind by making an indicated mountain fold.

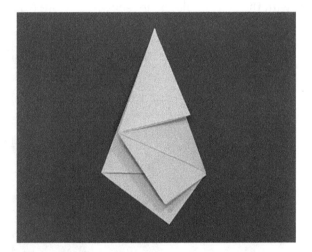

Figure 8.11.   After making the mountain fold.

The folding is complete. The final step is to make the cut. The cut starts on the right at the point indicated in Figure 8.12. The end point is to taste.

Figure 8.12.　Scissors shows direction of the cut.

The results, with the star unfolded, are shown in Figure 8.13.

Figure 8.13.　Five-pointed star and leftovers.

Square Letter O

Our folding for the Square Letter O systematically places all the edges on the same line and then makes the cut on that line. You can use this approach to discover (or is it invent) folding procedures for other shapes.

Figure 8.14 shows the pattern of the square O.

Figure 8.14. Pattern of the square O.

The next step was to fold the paper in the middle of the drawing to overlay the bottom with the top, as shown in Figures 8.15 and 8.16. Notice that we made this a mountain fold so that we could see the lines.

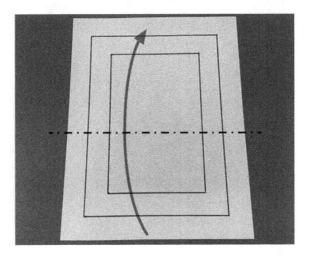

Figure 8.15. Mountain fold in the middle of the drawing.

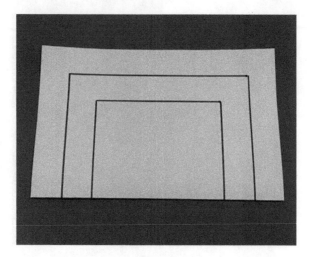

Figure 8.16.   Result of the mountain fold.

Next, we do a similar thing: this time folding the paper from right to left, that is, folding the paper to overlay the lines. See Figures 8.17 and 8.18.

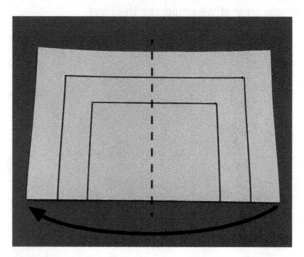

Figure 8.17.   Another fold to overlay the lines.

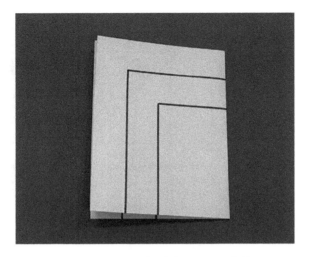

Figure 8.18. Result of the previous fold.

Our goal at this point in the process is to overlay the lines at the top with the lines on the left. This is possible by folding on the diagonal. See Figure 8.19, and the result is shown in Figure 8.20.

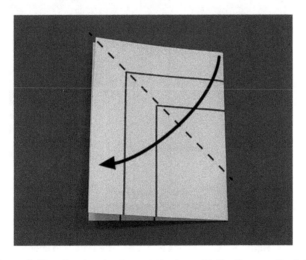

Figure 8.19. Overlay the lines at the top with the lines on the left.

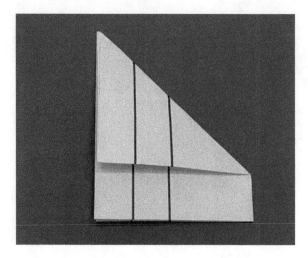

Figure 8.20.   Result of the previous fold.

Two distinct lines remain. The last step, pre-cutting, is to make a fold between the two lines as shown in Figure 8.21. Figure 8.22 shows the result.

Figure 8.21.   Making a fold between the two lines.

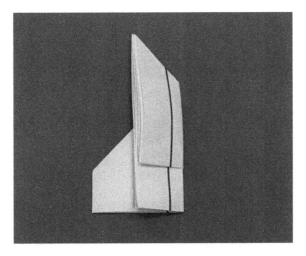

Figure 8.22. Result of the previous fold.

The cut is on the remaining line and indicated by the photo with a scissors shown in Figure 8.23.

Figure 8.23. Cutting the remaining line.

The result, unwrapped, is shown in Figure 8.24.

Figure 8.24. Square Letter O.

Initially, we thought that producing something with a hole might be difficult, but from this one example, it does not appear to be the case. What this example did have was symmetries and regularities (e.g., the width of the parts of the letter were the same) and our intuition is that this would reduce the number of distinct folds. In any case, try some more cases and follow up on the sources listed below to gain insight into the process.

Explanations

It is reasonable to ask the question: what shapes can be produced by folding a piece of paper and then doing a single, straight cut? It turns out that the types of shapes include not just what we can think of as simple polygons, but polygons with holes, groups of polygons, and, in fact, any collection of straight-line segments. Two distinct methods for producing the folding procedure have been developed by two overlapping sets of people. The intersection of the two groups is Erik Demaine, now a professor at MIT. Erik Demaine, Anna Lubiw, and Martin Demaine used what they describe as the *straight-skeleton* approach. Marshall Bern, David Eppstein, Barry Hayes and Erik Demaine developed a proof using a method they term *disk-packing*. These methods relate to Robert Lang's TreeMaker work, which he uses to produce crease patterns for models and work by Thomas Hull. More generally, just as the material on this book and **Origami with Explanations** relate to basic topics in mathematics, recent and current activity connect origami to advanced mathematics and computer science.

We note that part of this work and other work in origami mathematics is to establish the connection between the abstract concepts of straight lines manipulated in two and three dimensions and how actual paper is moved by folding. Though the two methods produce folding procedures for any shape in a large category of shapes, it may be that complex shapes could not be folded from real paper. There would be too many folds!

You can consult Erik's site (erikdemaine.org) and other sources for a description of the two methods, including a link to a video of his lecture on the topic. Erik also provides a brief history on folding and cutting, and cites as the first published reference a Japanese book, **Wakoku Chiyekurabe (Mathematical Contests)** by Kan Chu Sen, published in 1721.

Enhancements and Next Steps

This is our last chapter. Check out the Resources.

We hope that you will continue folding. This includes following the practices of Lillian Oppenheimer, Laura Kruskal, Mark Kennedy and Michael Shall to learn, share and teach origami with others. The site https://origamiusa.org/ provides a calendar of events in the USA along with a list of local groups. National origami organizations exist in many countries and many are listed in the OrigamiUSA site. We also urge you to experiment with making variations and inventing your own models and do not be concerned about the difference between these two activities. Lastly, do think about what you are doing in terms of mathematics, mathematics broadly defined (algebra, geometry, trigonometry, patterns, number theory, computing and spatial relations). The mathematics has its own beauty and origami and mathematics each will reinforce your understanding in the other area.

There are many applications of origami. Some artists incorporate origami models in their installations, and some 3D Computer Graphic designers use the knowledge of how to fold paper to make interesting animations. Origami has inspired work at a large scale: designing objects for delivery into space and on a small scale: designing objects for delivery inside the human body. Take advantage of what you have learned in this book and combine with whatever skills you have to explore new possibilities of origami!

Exercises and Explorations

1. Some websites recommend 8.5 × 10 for the star. We used normal 8.5 × 11. Try both and compare. Note that the method leaves the end point of the cut "to taste."
2. For Square Letter O, change the thickness of the letter (in other words, the width between two black lines). Experiment with different designs.
3. Pick a letter of the alphabet and see if you can fold paper to produce the letter with one-snip. Pick another letter. Try another alphabet.
4. Try to do some other shapes.
5. Go to erikdemaine.org and read about The Fold-and-Cut Problem.
6. Investigate the work of Robert Lang, especially his TreeMaker, and others cited in the Resources section.

Resources
(A listing of places to start your explorations)

OrigamiUSA (https://origamiusa.org/)

OrigamiUSA has listings for organizations around the world, local groups, and conferences as well as a store, called **The Source**, and online classes and workshops.

Books

Peter Engel, **Origami from Angelfish to Zen** + others.

Tomoko Fuse, **Origami Boxes** + others in English and in Japanese.

Gay Merrill Gross, **The Art of Paper Folding** + others.

Rona Gurkewitz and Bennett Arnstein, **Beginner's Book of Modular Origami Polyhedra: The Platonic Solids** + others.

Thomas Hull, **Project Origami: Activities for Exploring Mathematics**, 2nd edition, + others.

Robert Lang, **Twists, Tilings, and Tessellations: Mathematical Methods for Geometric Origami** + others.

John Montroll, **Origami and Math: Simple to Complex** + others.

Robert Neale and Thomas Hull, **Origami Plain and Simple**.

Jeremy Shafer, **Origami to Astonish and Amuse** + others.

Lewis Simon, Bennett Arnstein and Rona Gurkewitz, **Modular Origami Polyhedra**.

Websites (variety of personal websites, services, articles, programs, YouTube channels):

Gilad's Origami Website, *https://www.giladorigami.com/*.
Note: you can use this site to find designers of models and places to find instructions.

Sara Adams, *https://www.happyfolding.com/*.

Erik Demaine, *https://erikdemaine.org/*.

Miri Golan, *https://origametria.com/*.
A well-researched kindergarten and elementary school program

Thomas Hull, *http://origametry.net/*.

Paul Jackson, *http://www.origami-artist.com/*.

Beth Johnson, *http://bethjohnsonorigami.com/*.

Robert Lang, *https://langorigami.com/*.

David Mitchell, *http://www.origamiheaven.com/*.

Jeannine Mosely, *The Connective Power of Origami* by Davie Trueblood, *Technology Review*, August 18, 2015, *https://www.technologyreview.com/s/540661/ jeannine-mosely-sm-79-ee-80-phd-84/*.

Jo Nakashima, *https://jonakashima.com.br/*.

Jeremy Shafer, *https://www.youtube.com/jeremyshaferorigami*.

Index